Jean Arasanayagam was born to a Dutch Burgher family in Sri Lanka and is married to a Tamil. She studied at the University of Ceylon, Peradeniya, and at the University of Strathclyde, Glasgow.

She is a prolific writer and her poetry, fiction and plays have been widely published in Sri Lanka and abroad. Her work has been translated into French, German, Danish, Swedish, Japanese, Dutch.

She has received many awards for her writing. The most recent is the State Literary Award 1999 for her poetry collection *Women, All Women* (Writers Workshop, Calcutta).

Jean Arasanayagam lives and writes in Kandy.

BY THE SAME AUTHOR

Fiction

Peacocks and Dreams

The Outsider

All Is Burning

Fragments of a Journey

The Cry of the Kite

Poetry

Colonizer/Colonized

Women, All Women

Shooting the Floricans

Reddened Waters Flow Clear

Out of Our Prisons We Emerge

Trial by Terror

A Colonial Inheritance

Apocalypse '83

Poems of a Season Beginning and a Season Over

Kindura

JEAN ARASANAYAGAM

In the Garden Secretly
and Other Stories

PENGUIN BOOKS

Penguin Books India (P) Ltd., 11 Community Centre, Panchsheel Park, New Delhi 110 017, India
Penguin Books Ltd., 27 Wrights Lane, London W8 5TZ, UK
Penguin Putnam Inc., 375 Hudson Street, New York, NY 10014, USA
Penguin Books Australia Ltd., Ringwood, Victoria, Australia
Penguin Books Canada Ltd., 10 Alcorn Avenue, Suite 300, Toronto, Ontario M4V 3B2, Canada
Penguin Books (NZ) Ltd., Cnr Rosedale and Airborne Roads, Albany, Auckland, New Zealand

First published by Penguin Books India 2000

Copyright © Jean Arasanayagam 2000

10 9 8 7 6 5 4 3 2 1

Typeset in *PalmSprings* by SÜRYA, New Delhi
Printed at Chaman Offset Printers, New Delhi

'The Crossing' was first published in *Kunapipi*, University of Aarhus, Denmark

For my friends
Anna Rutherford, Ruth Carrington, Rajiva Wijesinha,
John Thieme, Seema Jena, Alka Nigam, Purabi Panwar and
Amitai Touval

Contents

Contents

A Note on the Stories

THE BACKDROP TO all the stories in this collection are the complex social and political scenario in Sri Lanka today. War and violence, radical political movements, dispossession and displacement are thus an integral part of the personal relationships in each story, within which context the individual search for enlightenment and self-realization must take place. Perhaps, it is the heightened sense of danger, the closeness to forces which threaten life itself that makes this search more urgent. Thus it is important to understand the specific context of each story.

The title story is set in the context of the seventeen-year struggle between the Tamil separatists and the state, of which the protagonist, an airman, is representative, and the divides which this causes between the north and the south of the island. This sense of division is also central to 'The Crossing'.

'Search my Mind' is set against the 1988-91 revolution in

the south of the island where the insurgents, named the 'Misguided Youth', were involved in an ideological struggle to destabilize the existing government and upset its status quo in the process. The protagonist is the teacher of English literature some of whose students are veterans of the earlier 1971 revolution, the Che Guevara Movement. 'Sanctuary' also harks back to the memory of the 1971 insurgency.

'Quail's Nest' explores the chaos and turmoil of ethnic upheaval in the latter part of the seventies, between the Tamil and Sinhala communities.

Both 'The Wall' and 'Samsara' speak of the changing communities in today's Sri Lanka.

In the Garden Secretly

DUSK. IN THIS terrain which grows slowly familiar to me, my feet in their dusty boots take exploratory steps. My hands do not let go of their firm grip on the T-56 rifle. I am wary. An eerie silence pervades the landscape. The sky is fringed with palmyrah fronds which look like dark wings. An abandoned village, once full of houses which are now only empty shells, bombed out. The palmyrah fences surrounding the ruins are ripped asunder, as if gigantic hands had torn them apart in a fit of rage. The armoured tanks had gone through them to avoid the pressure mines laid on the paths and roads. Such are the routes which invading armies take. The enormous wheels had crushed the fences that protected the privacy of lives of those who had once dwelt behind them, effaced the rituals and lives of whole families who had belonged to this village for generations, people whom we never knew and never would know.

All around me is complete silence. There are no human voices. The palmyrah fronds rustle in the slight breeze. A crow caws, a jarring sound. In the distance, there are other bird calls, which intensify my loneliness. And my sense of fear too . . . the fear of the unknown.

A house in front of me attracts my attention. The once-blue walls are shattered, the paint has peeled off and blistered. The roof has caved in. It is surrounded by trees, the branches of which are laden with ripening mangoes. There are also tamarind trees covered with golden yellow flowers, the ground below is strewn with fallen fruit. Bougainvillaeas spill cascades of sunset colours: pink shading into orange, white, purple, magenta, bright red. A lone jasmine bush is covered with white blooms. There is not a soul in sight. In the distance, I can hear the voices of my comrades making their own discoveries. We are all still alert. Terrorists may still remain hidden in pockets. We constantly look up at the trees—that's where snipers wait and watch.

I walk closer to the house. Blue walls are unusual. Perhaps it is a church. No, it can't be a church. It doesn't look like the usual church architecture. Some of the churches in this area are centuries old, I know, dating from Portuguese and Dutch times. American missionaries too had built churches, as well as schools and colleges. There were many conversions to Christianity. In the past, students from the south travelled north to study in these famous seats of learning. My grandfather had come to the north to study under the great scholars of his day.

I want to be by myself. Ever since I have come north, I have been plagued by this need to understand what I am doing here. The others in my company are elated, overcome by the euphoria of victory. They sing as our crowded trucks

4

lurch along the broken roads, swerve past the huge potholes. Those on foot move warily for there are lots of casualties from the landmines planted everywhere by the guerrillas in anticipation of our arrival. They see our every move as a gesture of aggrandizement. Yet we see ourselves as liberators. But do the people we think we are freeing see us in the same light?

The troops from the south have fought hard. Operation Sunrise I. We have moved into the very heart of the peninsula. Now we are all battle-worn and bone-weary. We haven't changed our uniforms or boots for days. We look like strange insects created out of this landscape of red earth, white sands and green-black leaves; our camouflage uniforms are the colour of the vegetation. The trucks and armoured tanks are also painted in camouflage patterns, like leaf-covered branches of trees. They look incongruous to me.

The landscape itself has been transformed by war. Sometimes it seems that only the camouflage patterns of our uniforms and vehicles provide the green. There are desolate spots which are populated solely by helmeted troops running through desecrated groves, with guns, in heavy boots, taking cover, lying down flat. There is the periodic splatter of machine gun fire. What do the bullets strike? The enemy is never seen. It is only on the army maps that the battles take place. The map of the peninsula shows thick black arrows, indicating the progress of the military campaign. Decisions are made in the boardrooms. Ground troops not enough, we need air power, naval power, gun boats, heavy artillery.

Guerilla warfare is never easy. I remember my history lessons. The Peninsular War, Spain, France, Ethiopia.

Guerrillas make the rulebooks of conventional warfare seem ridiculous. In the mountains, they use the natural formations of rock as cover. Here, in the thick jungles, they are impossible to find. But everywhere innocent people, uninvolved in the conflict, get caught up in the 'crossfire', that all-embracing euphemism used so often. Of course, in theory, one knows that civilian deaths are inevitable in any war. But I feel deeply uneasy. After all, now it's our own country that's being destroyed.

We all met after it was over, all of us who were part of Operation Sunrise I. The expressions on the faces of the men after they have reached the capital of the peninsula were like those of schoolboys after a victorious cricket match. A lethal match, but there is the same spirit of childish triumph though some of us have not made it.

Is it this boyish sense of triumph that impels men to go forward into unknown terrain? Our commanders try to inspire us before we set out on our forays. 'You are heroes, fighting for the motherland. Your patriotism will be rewarded. We are all together in this.'

I don't know why I am in this. Patriotism alone does not spur me on. I wonder why I am doing this when I fly over the peninsula, piloting the Sia Marchetti, the Avro or the Antonov. I ferry troops to the battlefield and support them in battle with air power, carry stocks of food and arms, and undertake reconnaisance flights. I also have to search out the military installations and training camps of the Tigers. When I see a military vehicle that might belong to them, I target it. It's not easy to find the exact position of their underground concrete bunkers, which are in the depths of the forest, concealed by palmyrah leaves. I know that a whole underground network of mazes lies hidden in the thick jungle; tunnels leading from village to village, to hospitals and ammunition dumps. Another life exists, buried deep. People live and breathe in the innermost depths of the earth. When I am flying, there is the excitement of knowing the seething life, the ingenious feats of engineering, exist unseen. What I can see is a mapped-out landscape: checkered patterns of red, brown, white, green and blue; cultivated fields, villages, townships, houses, *kovils* and churches, all toy-like and miniature.

War has its own distinctive language. A 'terrorist' is 'killed'. A 'soldier' 'sacrifices' his life. It's the eternal terminology, brought to fresh life in this current conflict. Who's to decide who is what, what is the difference between them? We're all groping blindly in the jungle, while day by day the war is carried deeper and deeper within, into our innermost beings. We too construct mazes within ourselves, tunnels through which our thoughts and feelings travel. Concealment and duplicity are now natural to us. We create our secret routes and travel through them, never emerging into the light of day.

In the beginning, for them, there was the Leader, who first took them in deep into those recesses. None of them could have gone in on their own. When they look upon the face of the Leader, it is not like seeing an ordinary man. The face that may seem colourless or even anonymous in times of peace takes on a heroic, epic aspect, like the deity whom you worship. So many thousands have been willing to die for the Leader, for the Cause. When that deified person dies, there is always another to take up his place, to inspire the people to queue up again, ready to be blasted to extinction, mutilated and maimed.

Sometimes I wonder what my own destiny is. I'm a pilot. Flying on missions gives a shape, a purpose, to my life. I like being up in the sky, far above terrestrial bonds. I have a friend, a monk who visits our home sometimes. He speaks of the *dewas*, the gods who dwell in clouds—be they warm clouds, thunder clouds, wind clouds, or rain clouds. I feel like a god myself when I am among the clouds, part of an exalted order. I have all kinds of fancies when I'm up there. I'm so much in control, much more than I am when I am down here. My mind takes on an agility that is unfamiliar to me. I feel I am a part of history. I want to possess a meaningful mission in a world filled with anonymous faces and unrecorded deeds. Perhaps that is what I want—to perform deeds which will sound like epics or the tales of war heroes I've idolized.

I know I am a hero and a patriot to some. But I'm not foolish, I also know what I am to others. I look down from the air at the peninsula. It looks so ordered, so patterned. But it's a pattern it is my mission to disrupt. War ceases to be black and white, heroic and epic because of the ordinary people who prevent the pattern from becoming neat. I remember a painting I saw in a book when I was in college. 'Guernica', that's what the art master called it. It showed the bombing of a village in the north of Spain, in Basque country. Province—what province was it? Viscaya. Yes. I remember the village in ruins, bombed buildings, the eyes of terror, the once-human truncated torsoes, snorting horses and bulls.

The image of the bullfight is central to the painting. The bomber is the matador. It is so similar to what I see around me: a civil war, the civilian population under attack; General Franco, the inspiring leader; distortions of death, fleeing figures, men, women and children; the savagery and carnage in remote villages. It was painted over half a century ago, around 1937. Guernica was bombed out with the help of an external power, the Germans. After death and burial, no boundaries exist. Memory, like quicklime, destroys the thought of that agony. None of us are whole human beings any more. Our eyes reflect the images of Guernica.

How does one tell a civilian from a guerilla from the height at which I fly? Ordinary people too construct bunkers in their gardens, and take shelter when they hear the bombers fly overhead. We have all suffered and grown wary in this war. Both sides.

Sometimes I wonder, will the war ever be over? When? Will we live to be old men? Will the record of our battles be documented in military histories? Is the history of a small island like ours important to the rest of the world? I like reading books about history, especially about the two World Wars: the Blitz, the fire-bombing of Dresden, Hiroshima. And the names in today's newspapers: Sarajevo, Grozny, Rwanda. The clouds everywhere are tinged with the colour of blood, the wind rings with the wails of the dying. Death is an everyday fact I live with. All of us are caught up in this vast obsession with death. We have all lost so many friends in this ceaseless fighting. I sometimes wonder what my last moments will be like. A plane crash? A landmine? A stray bullet intended for someone else?

We had come into the peninsula as victors. It should have been a triumphant entry. But there were no banners proclaiming our victory, no guards of honour, no red carpets, no grateful people to welcome our generals with garlands. The roads were quiet, the surface churned up by the movement of armoured tanks, jeeps, motorcycles and the straggling columns of soldiers. The people seemed to have all gone away, fled in the aftermath of the victory.

And so we walk through the silence and emptiness of the countryside and make our own discoveries. Strange ones sometimes: a Pleasure Park for the citizens, a palace which some say was the palace of their Leader, where the last supper was held before the suicide missions were undertaken, where they all posed for photographs with the Leader. It isn't really a palace, but a mansion that had once belonged to a wealthy citizen, with elaborate and ornate trappings and beautiful paintings. It is difficult to explain these things to the people of the south. After all, none of us have seen the almost-mythical figure of the Leader, no one knows very much about him.

After our victory, we had hoisted the lion flag of the south. The de facto state of the north has its own flag too, bearing the image of the tiger. The two beasts are in perpetual combat, forcing us deeper and deeper into the jungle, where the endangered species is man.

The silence here has a palpable quality, I can almost feel it shiver on my skin. I hold my T-56 more firmly in my hands. What an exodus must have taken place before we arrived! Terrible things must have been told about us, the invading armies from the south, the shelling heralding our

10

arrival. We think we are here to liberate the people here, though it is never specified who from. If they thought the same, why would they have fled?

And meanwhile there is the blue house. I step into it. This is not what I would have done in the south. If I were to visit a friend at home, I'd call out at the entrance, in anticipation of being greeted and welcomed. I would be asked news of common friends from the Air Force, from college, news about the fighting in the north and east. But for them, the war is very distant. Many of my friends in the south are still studying at the university or are young executives or bureaucrats. For them, my being in the Air Force has a kind of glamour attached to it. It makes them want to include me in the family. The parents of my friends, call me *putha* or son; to the sisters and younger brothers, I am *aiya* or elder brother.

Here in this empty house, I feel very alone. The peeling walls staring at me with animosity. The only sound I can hear is the echo of my footsteps on the cracked cement floor. There is no one to greet me, to offer me even a glass of water. Water has a different flavour here, tasting of this soil, this terrain. My friend Captain Pali says that the water in the well at the Fort Basilica at Pt. Pedro is clear and sweet. He is from a Kandyan village, and he says that the water from the springs and wells in his village is cool and fresh, and tastes of ferns and reeds. He's been in the army for ten years and has spent a lot of time in the peninsula. He believes that the other side fights with such single-minded intensity because they fight for a cause, their dream of a separate state in the north and east of the island. Eelam.

11

My home is at the southernmost tip of the island, close to the lighthouse at Dondra Head. I have often watched the strong beams light up the sea, there is a constant awareness that there may be danger to a boat at sea. There's no light here. Outside, it is growing darker and darker. I have a torch in my pocket, that will help me see my way through the empty rooms.

I feel a great sense of pity for the family who had lived here, whose home this was. I think of my home where my mother keeps everything in meticulous order. Every time I go back, my room is unchanged: the silver trophies on the shelves, the photographs of the college cricket and rugby teams, and old textbooks carefully preserved. There is order, a sense of life carrying on. I wonder where the people who lived here are now. Who were they, who lived in these rooms, walked in this garden and tended the plants and flowers? Did they willingly join the exodus out of the peninsula? Or were they forced to leave?

I push open a door. The wood is splintered, the door hanging on its hinges. Within the shadowy inner room, there is a strange luminous glow which emanates from a niche in the lime-washed brick wall, whose reflection flickers on the cracked glass windowpanes. It seems like a dim light bulb, but I know it cannot be that. There has been no electricity in the peninsula for some years now. I walk toward the niche, and am suddenly confronted by a statue of Jesus Christ. The people who had once lived here were Christians? We have that in common then: we worship the same god, pray to the same saints, chant the same litanies, though the language of the votaries would be different. But our prayers would still be the same: 'Give us this day our daily bread . . . Forgive us our trespasses, as we forgive them that trespass against us . . . Deliver us from evil . . . Thine is the Kingdom . . .

The statue glows, it seems, from both within and without, like the phosphorous lights that shimmer at the slightest ripple in the inky waters of Arugam Bay. The face, limbs and flowing robes of Christ shine, shedding light in the darkening corners of this empty shell. One arm of the statue is broken. I cannot see the expression on Christ's face, but does that matter? I am caught, transfixed between the incandescent glow of the statue and its fragmented reflection in the shattered glass.

This moment of intense calm does not belong to this place or time. All sounds of battle have receded from my consciousness. I feel an enormous sense of pity for the poor people who had to abandon their home and their shrine. The statue must have been a source of light and comfort to them, especially when darkness fell. Someone must have brought it for them from Europe, perhaps from Italy. And they had set it in this niche so that Christ could both physically and spiritually help them to see the light, in the darkness which was life on the peninusula these days. They must have looked upon the statue as a guardian in these uncertain and troubled times. Why did they choose to leave it behind? Couldn't they have carried it with them to wherever they were going, other parts of the peninsula or even beyond? I try to imagine the family who lived here—maybe there were young sons and daughters who are today asylum seekers in different parts of the world. Or are they involved in the struggle for Eelam?

I think of my brothers and sisters; think of them at this moment, as they surely must often think of me. What would I have felt if I had returned home to find it in ruins, walked into its emptiness with the hollow sound of my boots echoing in my ears? I am lucky, I have a home to go back to, a welcome to look forward to. In the south, we are now looked upon as heroes, patriots who are willing to sacrifice our lives for the motherland. And yet, it was not so long ago that we were regarded in a different light. When the revolution, the *bhishanaya*, was raging in our country, then the same army who had to put down the movement through violent means was looked upon with terror and hatred.

There are so many roles we have to play, and each involves duality and ambivalence. There are so many acts I commit, such as exhumations of the graves of dead subversives, that I have to justify. That the times were such, that we had to act as we did, that many saw us as their protectors. As example, we mention the border villages where they adore us, where parents are happy when their daughters marry a soldier.

Here, at this moment, alone in this shelled house, I wonder what the difference is between those who lived here and me. They have gone into exile. But in reality, we are in exile too. We have all been forced to leave the homes familiar to us, the lives that our families have lived for generations.

It must take so much courage to forge ahead, not knowing what lies before you, not bothering to lock the door behind you, for what is the point of locking up possessions that you will never see again? The bed you sleep on every night, the table you sit at, the mat you spread, things which are so

14

integral to your everyday life, suddenly become unimportant. Nothing matters any more but life itself. To live. You can take only what you can carry or load onto a cart which you have to draw yourself.

And when you leave, you do not know whether there will be a return. And even return can be bitter, if you come back to see your house in ruins, denuded of all you had lovingly filled it with, of all that made it your home, by invisible takers. That's when you realize most chillingly that return is not possible, that you have to start all over again.

How shall we sing the Lord's song, in a strange land?

We wept when we remembered Zion . . .

I am an intruder here, in an unknown person's house, yet it's difficult for me to walk out. I can't run away. I have to obey orders or I will be considered a deserter, court-martialled. I have to constantly obey, obey, obey. This is my only moment of solitude, of freedom from the all-pervasive rules and regulations which bind me.

There's something happening within me, it's not a sudden revelation, it's just that I feel . . . a sense of being human again . . . of having the luxury of having feelings, emotions—simple emotions—without the need to bring in the complexities of thinking. I feel for the owners of this house as I would feel for my own kith and kin, if they were placed in a similar situation. I want to help them to come back to their home, to get over that feeling of displacement, of being banished from the consciousness of the rest of the world. It's not just this luminous icon that makes me think, it's the abandoned village with its empty dwellings. I wonder what they all felt when they heard of our approach—we who see

15

ourselves as liberators on the most important mission of our lives. I remember a book I had read a long time ago where it said that at first Napoleon's armies were seen as liberators from reactionary autocratic governments. Yet things changed. Things always change . . . not always for the better . . .

I lean against a cracked wall. The light emanating from the icon seems to be almost from within, like stained glass windows in churches. Would I have knelt and prayed in the ruins of a church? Made the sign of the Cross? Our lives become meaningful now only if we think of them in terms of parables. There's the parable of the Good Samaritan, why isn't there a parable of an ordinary soldier? There's the story of the centurion's daughter, who was saved by faith. Many of my friends carry the ninety-first psalm in tiny leather pouches around their necks. I too possess a copy that my mother gave me, I finger the sacred words in their leather casing, and utter the words and phrases under my breath. There's one battalion commander who kneels down and prays with his men before they go out to battle. Their hallelujahs at the end of the prayer resound through the countryside. Casualties are supposed to be minimal in this battalion.

He is my refuge my fortress, with His wings He will cover me, shelter me. All the images we associate with Christ are protective, but what we pray for is at odds with what we do. Our missions often involve death. We seek to destroy, not forgive, our enemies.

Here, facing the statue of Christ, caught up in this silence, I interrogate myself. I look at the statue and try to think of the different names I know for him. The Saviour of

16

Mankind, Salvator Mundi, the Light of the World, the Good Shepherd, the Lamb of God . . .

The light emanating from the statue seems to be a symbol of the light of the world, it seems to be what I have been waiting for all these dark years.

The broken arm of Christ reminds me of Pali on the day that he was shot in his right arm and in his foot. He crawled in his own blood to reach safety, that strong instinct for survival impelling him. He would not have lived at all had not a boat drifted to a part of the coast where it was not supposed to be. No one should have survived. As it was, Pali survived, with thirty-six stitches in his arm. As he was convalescing in the army hospital in Colombo, watching the BMWs and the Pageros flashing by, the dancing on Galle Face Green, he told me he wondered if people knew at all that there was a war on in the north and the east? Would they need some cataclysmic event to make them realize? Pali's body had been awash with his own blood, his uniform and the dry earth along which he had crawled soaked. The militants were so close that he could see the expressions on their faces, intent on only one purpose, his destruction. He realized how intense that battle would be, outnumbered as the militants were. The women too engaged in battle, young girls . . . They are all completely convinced that they are fighting for the only cause that matters, he told me. Nothing else existed in their minds. Don't they remember Christ who shed His blood for us? How can they forget the communion service? Eat this in remembrance of me, drink this in remembrance of me. Go in peace . . . So much blood has already been shed, and there seems to be no sign of an end to the conflict.

17

What shall I do with this icon of Christ? I cannot bear to leave it in this ruined house. I know suffering was nothing new to Him: they scourged Him with whips, ridiculed Him. In His time, He was looked upon as a subversive element who dared to raise his voice against the mighty power of Rome. Yet today the names we remember Him by say nothing of His stand against temporal power, do they?

Shall I take the icon back with me to the camp and from thence to the south? I have no right to take it, but seeing Christ with the shattered arm, thinking of my wounded comrades and of the people who have gone away, I am overcome by feelings that I am not supposed to have. Don't take anything from peoples' houses, say the orders. I do not know whether I want to involuntarily transfer the pity I feel for the people to the broken icon of Christ, as a means of dealing with my emotions. And if it had been another image, another icon, another deity? I would have left it behind. I take hold of my T-56 in one hand. With the other, I carefully lower the statue from its niche, hold it close to my chest for a moment and then put it into my kitbag. I walk out of the house, looking around me carefully, both hands now free to hold the gun.

Search My Mind

I WAS RETURNING home from the teachers' training college where I teach when a young soldier stopped the van we were travelling in. He was standing guard near the gate of the Peradeniya Botanical Gardens. Behind him, the branches of the *ahela* trees were a mass of golden yellow flowers. But he seemed oblivious of them, intent only upon his duty and the T-56 rifle in his hands. The youth today carry burdens we never had to.

'Get off,' he commanded all the passengers peremptorily. 'You, stop there!' He indicated to the driver the spot, a little way ahead of us, where he wanted the van parked.

'Line up! Show me your bags! Open your parcels!'

We lined up obediently before him. One does not question a man with a gun. We were all tense and silent. It was 1988. The radicals were trying to topple the government, to destabilize the capitalist state. They believed that capitalism was immoral and alien to our land. Everyday life was disrupted by lightening strikes and protest campaigns. Overnight the walls were covered by posters bearing their slogans. Identity cards had to be surrendered to them. The transport systems in the cities were paralysed, checkpoints sprang up everywhere, and tea factories were set ablaze. There were many tales of sporadic violence, and rumours of arrests, disappearances, detention camps and deaths. Indoctrination cells and safe houses were being increasingly mentioned.

I stood before this young soldier and showed him the contents of my shabby, well-worn leather bag. Text books: *The Merchant of Venice* and *The Village in the Jungle*. Some fifty-cent and one-rupee coins for the van. The conductors grumble if you didn't have the correct change. A few exercise books containing lecture notes, with half-finished poems written on the last pages, poems which which nobody read.

The soldier peered in dispassionately. I wondered what he expected to find in the bag of a middle-aged teacher of English literature. A time bomb? Firearms?

Finally all the bags were inspected and we were told we could move on. We walked past him in silence, climbed into the van and were driven off. No one uttered a word.

In times before the troubles began, one saw young men and women from the university, which lay just beyond the crossing, sitting in pairs, lost in their private world beneath the shady trees of the gardens. Beside the gardens, there is an intersection where many roads meet. There is a small grassy plot there, which used to be filled with brilliantly-coloured beds of canna lillies and colias, interspersed with small trees with feathery leaves. There also used to be a signboard there, saying 'Welcome to Kandy'. Now there was a small encampment of soldiers on that plot, and it was covered by canvas tents. The young soldiers gazed with indifference at the roads around them. I wondered about the journeys which these soldiers observe. Many journeys from the nearby university now, I was sure, were those with no return. After all, this was where many of radicals belonged, from where young men were taken away in locked vans. Through the barred windows, you could see only the backs of their heads.

The van passed the spot where I had taken a walk earlier today with Soma, who works in the kitchens of the teachers' training college. This used to be the royal gardens of the Kandyan kings, a beautiful place filled with kitul palms, breadfruit and mango trees. She told me disturbing rumours of what was happening in the various colleges. The young clerk of the training college had been arrested. One of the assistant superintendents of the hostel had been killed. It was whispered that he was an informer. His body was found abandoned one morning with gunshot wounds, beneath the spreading branches of a mango tree. A senior registrar of the University had also been killed by insurgents. There were retaliatory killings soon after. Fifteen insurgents had been decapitated, their heads arranged around the ornamental pond at the centre of the university campus. No one could go anywhere in the university without passing this spot and seeing these bizzare new additions to the landscaped garden.

'We are sinners,' Soma said. 'That is why we have to see such sights. Yesterday there was one body burning on the road, with tyres placed on it. Today it is still burning. Yesterday, the face was recognizable. Today, it's a charred mass. My daughter was with me today. She wanted to go

23

closer and look at it. I told her, "Mala, I'll thrash you if you speak about it to anyone." Just burning, burning. Must have been a young man—his hair was thick and black.'

Every day, the world changes around us, especially among the young. On my way to work, I saw schoolboys with handkerchiefs tied across their faces like masks to ward off the fumes of burning tyres set up as roadblocks. A crowd of schoolboys from one of the government schools crowded around the gates of a leading private college, urging these students to join their protest march.

Another day, on the way from work in a private bus, I saw some schoolchildren standing on the grounds of their deserted school, hurling stones at passing buses. Our bus slowed down to a crawl, and I held up my bag to ward off the stones. A schoolgirl came up to the bus to reassure us. 'The stones are only thrown at the state buses,' she announced calmly. Many buses now have slogans in thick black paint scrawled across their metal bodies. Posters are pasted on every available bit of space—walls, lamp posts—criticizing the government and its leaders.

Children stop the van I usually travel on, board it, and hold out empty tins for collections. They buy firecrackers with the money. You can hear the intermittent bursts as they explode. Students are shot while they demonstrate. Buses are burnt. Bus drivers are shot for disregarding the orders of the insurgents. White flags are hung across on ropes and barriers of old rubber tyres are placed on the road. Processions of students, carrying white banners proclaiming their protests, march on the streets. The police jeeps crawl beside them. They dare not do anything to the protesters. The arrests come later.

Nowadays as the troubles draw close again, I began to question my own role in teaching English literature to students who left the classroom to tear down the edifices of the past. On the ruined walls, they scrawled their own burning messages. I had to find parallels and relevance to this reality in my lectures. I had been out of the country for many years and the new faces of our youth were revelatory.

In the staff room, colleagues discussed their experiences of the day. Clement said, 'We heard the sound of gunshots last night near our home in Bowala. I went early in the morning to investigate. I had a good look at the corpses. Blindfolded. Hands tied behind back and shot. The milkman passed by at that moment. No one came to claim the bodies.'

'Life goes on as usual?' I queried.

'Of course,' replied Clement. 'How else are we to live?'

The images permeated the assignments that my students handed in to me. Shantha, one of the quietest students in my class, wrote, 'A body is swung in a hammock over a fire, roasting. The men sit around. They dip their bloody fingers into tins of savoury biscuits. The smell of the burnt flesh pervades the cool night air.' What images are our children growing up with?

Our nights are filled with the sound of gunshots and surreal dreams. Daylight astounds us as we wake. We feel ourselves spectres and phantoms, spirits emerging from the grave.

The attendance in my classes starts diminishing, especially the older students, the veterans of the 1971 insurgency who had returned to college. These were the students who I felt were more dedicated to their work. They had experienced so much that they were incapable of the youthful frivolity of some of my other younger students. Especially two of them, to whom I was very close. Perhaps they felt more able to relate to an older woman than their fresh-faced young classmates.

Sumedha had led a prison riot at Bogambara jail for better conditions for the political prisoners when he was imprisoned there after 1971 insurgency. He showed me the bullet scars on his neck and told me stories of his prison experiences. 'I got shot but escaped with my life. I was helped later on to get back to life after my release, with the help of a Roman Catholic priest . . . He said I should be a teacher, which is why I am here . . .'

Sumedha was always irregular in attendance. Now, after the troubles started again, he began to disappear more regularly, sometimes for weeks. His home is in the village of Mahawa, in Wanni, the north central province of the island. I know the area well. My family has coconut plantations there. The 1971 insurgency had been deeply entrenched in that region. I think that he probably goes back to organize lectures for new recruits from his village. But I know he feels it is important for him to get his teachers' qualifications. So he suddenly came back to lectures, just before the examinations. 'Madam, let's get on with the text. I've got to catch up with what I've missed.'

I asked him once about how he felt about the failure of the insurgency, what it was that drove the young to sacrifice all. He was passionate in his explanation. 'Madam, at least we have taken one step forward, for the revolution.'

My other pupil who was in the 1971 insurgency is Saman. He told me that he was inculcated into the insurrection when he was very young. 'I was in school. My teacher indoctrinated me. I was in one of the attacks on a police post. Was arrested. Spent six years in prison. Tortured. Strung up from the roof beams.' He told me the story of how he was arrested. The boys had planned an attack on a police station. But the policemen had been forewarned and they were prepared for them. When the busload of students arrived the policemen were all in position, perched on the branches of trees around the station, camouflaged behind the leaves. They had shot a stream of bullets into the bus. By the end, the floor and seats were awash with blood. All the boys were killed or arrested. Saman also told me of his six-year ordeal in prison, and showed me some roughly-written pages about his experiences. I had sent the manuscript to an English literary journal, but it had not been accepted. As the troubles started again, Saman too became more and more irregular in attending classes.

Meanwhile, we tried to carry on classes as normal, tried to have our usual writers' workshops and seminars. But this resulted in a brutal reminder that all was not well as many academics and writers from Colombo and further away now refused to come to Kandy. They thought it was too dangerous.

In the end, we were able to organize just one seminar. Ricardo, a young poet, actor and theatre director, came one day to talk about his favourite play, *The Merchant of Venice*. Ricardo was something of a cult figure—his poems and plays have provided a new and exciting cultural forum for many. For once, the lecture theatre was crowded in a way it had not been for months. In the corner, I saw both Saman and Sumedha.

Ricardo was rivetting that night. With his richly resonant voice and charismatic personality, he presented the play to us in terms of the reality of our own lives and times. For us, he said, as for the Venetians, life was so fragmented. For us, there was the revolution in the south as well as the ethnic conflict between the majority Sinhala community and the militant Tamil guerilla forces fighting for a separate homeland in the north and north-east of the island. But we should not let our vision be blinkered by where a person came from, he argued passionately. 'Look at this room,' he declaimed. 'There are students from all the communities—Sinhalese, Tamils, Muslims. This is the kind of unity we need to aim for.' The Christians of Venice were racist, he explained. They persecuted Shylock because he belonged to the minority Jewish community. I could see my students getting wide-eyed as they listened to him, the play taking on a new meaning in their eyes. Who could have known then that Ricardo would be abducted from his home one night, tortured and murdered? His bullet-ridden body would be dropped into the sea from a helicopter, and later washed ashore to be discovered by a fisherman.

Every evening, the lights went off in our housing colony. The roads too were dark. All doors were firmly locked and all windows shut in each house. Each householder had put up new protective barriers around his property. Some had built walls; others, like us, had propped up the sagging old iron gates and straightened the barbed wire fence to demarcate the boundary between ourselves and the world of threatening darkness outside. Those barriers would turn out to be too fragile. Nothing could withstand the radical forces of the changing times. All traffic ceased after nightfall. The sound of each lone motorbike on the road brought a cold chilling sense of fear to the heart. But it always passed on, and we breathed a sigh of relief, yet felt compassion for the people of whichever house it had stopped in front of.

One evening, the motorbike stopped at our gate. The gate creaked open, dragging against the pebbles and sand with a rasping sound. Each of us, in our own rooms, raised our heads to follow the sounds. Footsteps, treading lightly, came towards the front door. Then there were light staccato taps on the wood, which sounded as if they were made by a clenched fist.

My husband emerged from the study where he was reading *An Historical Relation of Ceylon* by Robert Knox, who had been a prisoner in the Kandyan kingdom from 1659 to 1697.

'Who is this at such an ungodly hour?' I turned to him to ask softly.

'We shouldn't open the door to anyone,' Raj was insistent.

Rima, my elder daughter, had not heard the sounds for she had been in the kitchen. Hearing our voices, she called out to us. 'I've heated the food. It's on the table. Let's finish our meal early so that we can turn off the lights. We shouldn't attract attention to the house.' She was a student at the University. When she received no response, she came out into the hall and saw us standing huddled there, staring at the silent door.

'Did someone knock on the door?' she asked us. We

stood there, still silent.

'It must be one of them,' she said. 'They come at this hour generally.'

There was a second knock on the door, more insistent this time.

'Open the door. We have to find out who it is,' I told Raj.

'Don't open it! That would be folly!' Rima said. It was uncharacteristic for this calm daughter of mine to get agitated, but maybe she knew much more than we do about what was happening.

But Raj, murmuring 'just investigate . . .', had already turned the key in the lock, half-opened the door and was peering out into the darkness.

There are two figures on the threshold, two young men in leather jackets and crash helmets. The one in front was held up by the second one, who had one arm around his waist and the other behind his sagging shoulders.

I peered into their faces through the helmets. I recognized the one in front, it was Saman. The other, whose face was in the shadows, I did not know.

'It's Saman. One of my students. I know him,' I told Raj.

Saman and his friend stood on the step at the door, and it was as if this was a scene from the past which I had read about and heard about, and which was now being enacted in front of me. It was not something I had ever imagined I would actually see. Saman slowly unzipped his jacket and removed his crash helmet with great effort. Blood had seeped from his wounds, his hair was caked with blood and mud.

His first words were tentative. 'Madam, I need your help. I trust only you.'

'Saman, where have you been all these weeks? You appear suddenly like this . . .' I said. I felt the futility of my question—where would he have been but with others from the movement? But I had no reaction adequate to the situation.

'Madam,' he stammered, 'madam, so many of us arrested . . . holding classes for the new recruits . . . others who were putting up posters . . . we were all taken to a detention centre, in a Roman Catholic college, opposite an army camp . . . Last night, ten of us were taken out of the city in a truck, far out into the countryside . . . We were all blindfolded, hands tied behind our backs . . . lined up . . . shot . . . several shots . . . I fell . . . felt bodies, limbs, twitching, writhing in the throes of death . . . So I lay there, pretending to be dead too . . . After a long time, they left. I waited even longer. Then I crawled into the undergrowth . . . huge leaves cool against my body . . . pain, blood, mine and that of those dead. Finally I got up. There was not a soul in sight. I staggered like a blind man along the stream, and reached Rohitha's place. He lives close by . . . Madam . . .'

Rohitha spoke out of the pool of darkness by the door. His words were clipped, but his voice was firm and authoritative. 'Shelter for the night. Till we attend to the injuries. Shift him to a safe house tomorrow.'

We were still all at the door, but we couldn't remain there forever. The blood splotch was growing larger on Saman's white shirt, a student's shirt. His face was ashen.

'Madam,' he pleads. 'Madam, you taught us, remember? *The Merchant of Venice*. There is that bit in it: "The quality of mercy . . . is not strained . . ." ' In his exhaustion, the words come out slowly.

31

Rima had been standing quietly at the back, her stiff posture indicating her reluctance to have anything to do with Saman. Now suddenly she came forward to continue the lines Saman seemed to be too weak to quote:

It droppeth as the gentle dew from heaven

Upon the place beneath. It is twice blessed . . .

Raj opened the door wider. We stretched out our hands to help Saman in. In this time of darkness, we need all the blessings which we can get.

Saman staggered into the drawing room. Rohitha turned away and vanished into the darkness. We closed the door and locked it. Outside, the motorbike revved up and departed. Silence enveloped our road again. We switched off all lights. I lit a candle and we led Saman into an inner room.

Tomorrow I will read the trial scene, act iv, scene i, of *The Merchant of Venice* with my students. I will refresh their memories of all that has gone before. And what will happen again and yet again.

Quail's Nest

NEITHER MY HUSBAND nor I had been able to catch a wink of sleep all night. We sat huddled together, leaning against the headboard, trying to protect our children. Anxiety kept our eyelids open, although the darkness pressed against them. Every light in the house switched off, every window was shut. The doors were all securely fastened. I stared through the windows at the dim outline of the landscape of fear outside. Beyond the garden, beyond the hill on which our house stood, the valley spread before us with hidden pathways leading to tea estates, tea factories, temples and *viharas*. The silent river glistened in the moonlight as it wound between the paddy fields and thickly wooded banks. The mountain ranges stretched along a darkened horizon.

The only sounds of the night were of the cries of cicadas and the occasional startled bird. My eardrums throbbed with the silence.

I got up from the bed quietly so that my sick daughter would not be disturbed, and crept to the window. I drew aside a shadowy curtain. There was not a soul was to be seen. Curfew was on.

My vigilant husband called me back in a harsh whisper. 'Don't let yourself to be seen. Anyone might be out there, behind the trees. I should have lopped off those branches. They could be anywhere, behind the house, or on their way here . . . I think her fever is rising. Touch her forehead, see . . .'

I tiptoed back to the bed, sat down and stroked the dank hair of my sleeping daughter. She was shivering, yet the heat of her forehead seared my palm. I covered her with sheets and blankets to keep her warm. I soaked a strip of cloth in eau de cologne and water, and laid it on her forehead. The heat soon dried the cloth.

My husband and I talked in whispers.

'So many doors in this house . . .'

'From where do we escape if they surround us?'

'Where can we flee?'

'The old burial grounds of the village behind the house . . .'

'Isolated on this hill . . .'

'Lovers met there often, remember?'

'No one to disturb or interrupt them . . .'

'That moonlight night when we went there . . . the woman with her hair streaming about her . . . limbs all silver . . . undergrowth rustling . . .'

'Need not have been afraid . . . only animals.'

'But they had gone away . . . night had swallowed them up . . .'

Nightfall had brought no comfort. Yet we had longed for these moments of peace, of respite, of darkness, all day.

Throughout the morning, there had been news of the escalating violence coming in. All we could do was to listen to the rumours that were spreading like wild fire. For the first time, I began to understand what fear was, the fear of being thought alien, of being the other. Those metaphors of violence and alienation that I had taught my students in the classroom now were coming true for me, jolting me out of the secure life I had always taken for granted, assumed would never change. Now suddenly, because my husband was Tamil, it was as if we were different, as if we no longer had the right to belong, to be part of the community.

'Where can we go? How can we take a sick child with us?'

My daughter mumbled in her sleep and turned over, as if responding to us talking about her.

The family doctor had come to see her that afternoon, dapper and immaculate as usual in his starched white suit. He had sat calmly on the edge of her bed, taken her temperature, checked her heartbeat and pulse. He had nodded gravely as he had shaken down the mercury in the thermometer and given us instructions about what medicines to get from the dispensary. Dr Winn had been my doctor when I was a child, had attended to every childhood ailment that I had had. In time, I had taken my children to him too. I had faith that he could cure every disease. Yet now I knew he was powerless to record the intensity of the fever of fear we were experiencing. And he could not cure it.

No, there would be no sleep for us, natural, restoring, dream-filled sleep, for a long, long while.

I went up to the window again, compulsively drawn to

the stillness and silence of the night. I opened a slit and peered out through it. Down in the valley, there were shadowy figures on the road leading to the Sivalingams' dark house, the very house that had been pillaged that morning. They pushed the gate open, went into the garden, and then some of them went up the steps leading to the house. The silence of the night was broken by heavy thuds as they started battering down the door. I could hear their voices, a low excited babble. Then I saw the lights of jeeps from the police post set up nearby race along the lower road and stop at the house. The policemen leaped out, and screams of pain rang out as batons were wielded on those shadowy assailants. It was as though I was watching a film. I felt so detached from the sequence of events. The policemen rounded up the assailants, loaded them onto the jeep and drove off. By now, the lights had come on in the house, and in the houses of the neighbours, all of which had been wrapped in darkness. Then once more the tiny beacons were put out and the valley was silent.

I went back to the bed and touched my daughter's forehead again. The fever had not abated.

I will light a hundred candles when she recovers, I promised myself. When the troubles are over, I will go on pilgrimage to the most sacred shrines in the land . . .

It had all begun so suddenly. It was hard to believe that it was only this morning that we had heard that there had been a clash between the police and a section of the Tamil community in the north, in the town of Jaffna. On the radio news, they had said that the violence was spreading all through the island. Indefinite curfew had been declared in many places. No one knew what would happen next.

I decided that before curfew was declared in our village, I should stock up food for the family. Once curfew was on, I knew it would be impossible to get food. I would have to go to the only grocery shop in the village, which was down the hill, on the river road.

'I will go by myself. It will be safer that way,' I told my children. I did not really feel there was any danger in our community. There were many Tamil families. But somehow I felt impelled to go alone. My husband and the children stood on the crest of the hill, their figures outlined against the white skyline, watching my lonely journey.

There were long queues rapidly forming at the store. Everyone was on the same mission: trying to buy as much as possible of rice, dal, sugar and vegetables. The sacks of rice were soon emptied, the baskets of vegetables vanished.

I set off for home with my bags filled with whatever I had been able to get. The house on the hill seemed so far away. As I walked down the river road, I could see a motley band of young men, striplings most of them, walking towards me from the direction of the neighbouring villages of Arucolla, Lewella and Sirimalwatte, which was across the river. They had tucked up their sarongs so that they could walk freely, and they brandished their wooden poles and roughly-hewn clubs. I had taught some of them. They knew who I was, a teacher married to a Tamil.

There was nothing I could do but walk on the extreme edge of the road, hoping that the sunflower bushes would camouflage or at least half-conceal me. I wished that I could take on the colour of the red earth, transform myself into one of the wild almond trees that grew by the road. We had to pass one another. As we drew nearer, they seemed to veer in my direction. The wooden clubs and poles almost touched me. I saw the rough grain of the wood, the darkness of their eyes. The sound of the rushing river waters was drowned by their voices . . . I held my bags of food before me; the shield they made was frail indeed.

In that brief moment, as we faced one another, I thought of the night when we had been guests at a performance of one of the Jataka stories, during the Wesak celebrations at Nittawala, organized by the Muslim owner of a joss-stick factory. We had been the chief guests and had sat in the front row, amidst the crowd of villagers and visitors from other villages. That night, I could not have imagined anyone wanting to harm me. They performed the story of the Bodhisattva who was born as the weakest of a quail's nestlings. One day there was a forest fire, and all the animals and birds of the forest fled before it. The other nestlings in the quail's nest flew off, leaving the weakest one behind. The fire raged through the forest, igniting the dry leaves and twigs. But the Bodhisattva knew no fear, for he was protected by the power of truth. When the fire reached the nest, he had addressed it gently. 'I am not strong enough to fly away, and my parents and brothers have fled for fear of you. Agni, god of fire, there is no gift here worth offering to you. So I ask you in the name of Truth, for which I have lived and now live, to turn back.' The ferocious fire stopped.

By this time, the group had passed by me, and walked on along the road. Looking up at the hill, my home now seemed like a watchtower, a fortress. I saw my family lined up like sentries. They had seen my encounter with the mob.

As I rounded a bend on the road, I saw my friend Lillian standing by her garden fence. She belonged to the Sinhala community, but her husband Joe was Tamil. She cried out as soon as she saw me. 'What shall we do? What shall we do?' She wrung her hands. 'Joe is hiding in the house. But how long can we keep him? He's a danger to himself, a danger to us all.' There was nothing I could say to her, but her fear made me afraid.

Like a cat, I crept along. The road seemed unending, and empty. Unlike other days, there was no one at the river, diving, swimming, bathing, washing clothes, scrubbing one another's back . . .

One lone man appeared as if from nowhere. He walked rapidly past me, muttering as he went, 'Telephone, I am looking for a telephone. The mobs are planning to attack the Tamil houses. I have to call the police.'

I climbed laboriously up the hill with my bags of food. The slope had never seemed so steep. My children ran to embrace me. 'Ma, Ma, you're safe? We watched everything from here. Dad wanted to come down and meet you halfway but we stopped him.'

We did not go inside the house, but stood and watched the winding progress of the group of men I had passed as they strode through the valley. They looked like little toy figures. We could see where they were headed now—to the Sivalingams' house. They walked purposefully through the gates, went up the steps like guests who were expected. They had an air of nonchalant assurance, as if accustomed to the house, familiar with the family who dwelt there. The

Sivalingams' eldest son Ramesh opened the door, flattened himself against it and allowed the men to walk in. They disappeared inside. No one hindered them. We stood watching from the top of the hill. There was a brooding silence. After some time, about fifteen minutes or so, they came out carrying, staggering under the weight of the loot. One man helped another to lift a sack of goods. It all seemed so normal. No unusual sounds disrupted the quiet morning.

I looked up at the brilliant green fields stretching across the valley. It seemed like any other day. Nature appeared to be undisturbed. When I looked down at the road again, the now-familiar group was making its way back. We went inside, and soon my daughter began burning with high fever.

We spent the evening like most other evenings, sitting in our drawing room, but we listened to the news on the wireless with a new concentration. I had not gone for my usual evening walk by the river. It was cold and dark, sheets of rain were falling outside. Leaves drifted like shadowy fish on the windowpanes. I tried to occupy myself by designing elaborate embroidered tapestries for some friends. I was trying to base the design on the plumeria tree in my garden. It looked like the tree of life.

'I need silk,' I told my husband.

'I could go to town . . .' he began, but this just brought home to us all the events of the day that we had been trying to forget. We both knew it was not safe for him to go to town. Also, the roads were empty. There was not a bus in sight. Everyone seemed to have taken cover in their homes. He could not have gone to town even if he had wanted to.

I think it was the communal nature of the disturbances which troubled us, especially because they came so soon after the victory for the new ruling party at the elections. There had been sporadic disturbances between the defeated party and the victorious one. At the dead of night, the house of a leader of the Opposition in a nearby village had been attacked, all the glass windowpanes shattered. A gang of youths from the village had crept up to the sub-postmaster's house, flung stones at the windows and the roof, and melted away into the night. But all these people belonged to the same Sinhala community, their differences were only political.

After the elections, we all had hoped for a new Utopia. We wanted to forget the bread queues, which had sometimes been baton-charged by the police when the crowd was unruly. A loaf of bread had been a trophy of victory, carefully sliced and shared among the family. Those who possessed paddy fields and rice aplenty, boiled the rice, packed it in woven baskets and carried it to their friends and relatives as they were not allowed to take the paddy. There was no milk powder for infants; one had to search for milk far and wide. The only cloth available—cheap printed material—often smelt strongly of kerosene. There were no toys for children.

We had thought that a golden age of equality would begin when the new government came into power. There was a ceiling imposed on the number of houses a landlord could own, the number of acres he and his family could farm. The Indian workers who were employed on the large plantations were now left without jobs. They wandered through the streets of Kandy, sleeping on pavements, begging for food, waiting for repatriation to their homes in the south of the subcontinent. The people seemed to have forgotten the 1958 communal violence and the 1971 insurgency, burying the memories deep within their psyches. They were not aware, or were unwilling to acknowledge, that the movement had only gone underground, and that it could be resusciated at a time which no one yet could foresee or predict.

And now in 1977, it had begun all over again. But in our little community, where both ethnic groups had always lived in harmony, we had believed that the violence would not touch us.

That evening, sitting in the security of our drawing room, I looked at my children. Their identity and inheritance would always make them feel they were a race apart in their homeland. My husband had experienced this alienation as a young student in 1958. He had been taking examinations for an Honours degree in Economics, when Emergency was declared and all examinations abruptly cancelled. However, he had had many friends in the security forces who helped safeguard his home and family. He had told us story after story of those who had managed to escape the mobs—one man had hidden for hours in his water tank, breathing like a fish within it, while the mobs rampaged through his house. A young woman he knew had taken shelter in the house of an old fisherwoman on the beach. A child in Polonnaruwa had been put into a barrel of tar.

I knew many tales of horrors from that year. 'We were hiding in attics,' my friend Chandra had told me. 'And my baby was just three months old! Although we had friends, it did not seen fair to put them into danger by hiding in their houses. Though only few of them offered. Some people we had been close to merely said, "Go elsewhere".'

My friend Lorna had been in the process of moving to Colombo from Amparai, in the eastern province, when the trouble broke out. A Tamil had come up to them and pleaded for safe passage to Colombo as he would surely be killed if he stayed on there. 'There was only one way in which we could take him,' she told me. 'We were taking all our furniture with us in a lorry. We hid him in the cane dirty-linen basket. On the way the mobs stopped us but we were able to escape. That was only because we are Burghers, not involved in the ethnic violence. The man was trembling with fear in the basket, but we managed to take him safely to Colombo.'

As we sat in the drawing room, each of us wrapped in our own thoughts, our neighbour Mrs Ismail called out to us from over the garden fence, her voice shrill with anxiety. 'Don't you people know what's happening? The Balasingham house has been attacked, the mobs are inside. The same has happened to the Loganathans. The Hanguranketa family heard the terrifying cries . . . We must see that they are at least safe . . .' Mrs Ismail was a very brave, so were our other neighbours. They would give shelter and take these people in, provide them with safety on that night of terror. I could not go with them for my daughter needed me. And it would be unwise for my husband to go out.

And then began this night of no sleep. Towards dawn, I heard loud shouts and the crackle of fire. But I was too terrified to go out and look.

When it was finally light, I walked out into the garden and saw what it was. Smoke still billowed out of the

Balasinghams' house, which had been reduced to a charred frame.

'Go in, go in, can't you see that they are burning the house?' Mrs Ismail called out to me frantically. 'You only put yourself in danger when you come out and draw attention to yourself.' She came over to my house some time later and told me that the Balasinghams and the Loganathans had been given shelter with neighbours.

As she left, my friend Deborah, an English medical student, came up the drive with paper bags full of food for our family.

'Deborah!' I welcomed her with a warm embrace. 'Why did you came through all these disturbances, especially to our house of all houses?' I was touched by her gesture, but worried at the same time.

'How could I not come? You of all my friends . . . You can't stay here any longer . . . Come with me to England!'

I smiled. I was not prepared for exile yet. I led her to the drawing room, remembering the first time she had come to my house, to learn batik painting from me. We soon became friends, and she would come over regularly from the guest house in Kandy where she was living. One morning she had brought her guitar and sung ballads to us, of which my favourite was 'Scarborough Fair'.

Are you going to Scarborough fair?
Parsley, sage, rosemary and thyme.
Remember me to one who lives there,
She was once a true love of mine.

Our very different worlds came together. She watched me draw the fabulous and mythical *garuda* or double-headed

46

eagle, the *nari-lathas* whose torsoes sprang out of tendrils and vines, the *kinduri* who were half-bird, half-human, elephants sporting in lotus pools, stylized flowers and foliage that sprang from a world that existed only in the imagination of the ancient and anonymous artists who had painted the flags and temples of my land. And as she watched, she sang ballads and told me stories of her family, of their home in the Isle of Wight, how it was so cold there that she would run straight to bed after supper, snuggle under her blankets to keep warm in the unheated bedroom. And those little human details that made her family come alive to us, that her father grew vegetables, her mother was an excellent sportswoman and her sister was very shy . . .

'Parsley, sage, rosemary and thyme . . .' Our friendship developed over food, she told me about English herbs while I introduced her to Sinhala delicacies. How amazed she was when I served her sausages and mashed potatoes one day! 'Bangers and mash,' I had announced, bringing the steaming pan off the fire. Bangers and mash, so obviously a phrase belonging to another culture, associated with other unfamiliar foods, of bubble and squeak, of Yorkshire pudding, roast beef and horseradish sauce. Deborah and I were moving in and out of each other's worlds. Seeing her today suddenly made the world feel normal and I half-forgot what was happening outside.

As we sat down, Ranmenike came in. She looked distraught and exhausted. She had run all the way from Davy Road to my house.

'The mobs are on their way to your house . . . They said they are coming to attack and burn batik *mahatthaya's* house.'

She wiped her flushed face with the edge of her sari. 'The men have gathered at the roundabout and will soon be here. Run. Take the children and escape. Don't delay, run, run.'

This was it then. The end. Soon our house too would be reduced to a charred mass. Yet at this moment all I can think of is how much Ranmenike had risked. And my fears about Deborah.

Ranmenike and her daughters Nanda and Kumari came to my house every day to help me with batik work and embroidery. My daughters are close to her daughters, and they entertain each other by singing their *kavi* and doing their intricate steps of the *udarata natum*, the Kandyan dancing they had learnt in their village schools.

'If you don't go at once, it will be too late . . . Who can save you?' Ranmenike pleaded tearfully.

I put my arm round Ranmenike's shoulders. I could feel the heat of her body through her cotton jacket, and the tears on her cheeks as I laid mine against hers. 'Go home safely,' I told her. 'Don't put yourself in danger . . . I must look after Deborah and see that she goes back to Kandy safely!' I looked at Ranmenike sadly. 'Where can we go? There is no safe place, no refuge. We cannot put our friends into danger. They will seek us out . . . And my daughter is too ill to be taken anywhere . . . We shall have to remain here.'

Ranmenike left. She would encounter the mobs on her way back. They would have known what her mission was. But she was a strong woman. She had risked her safety to warn us.

My fears were now for Deborah, stranded among us, unable to go back to Kandy, in a house that would soon be

48

attacked and burned.

'We will see that no harm comes to you,' I told her.

'I will walk to Kandy from here. It's a distance of about three kilometres. I can do it,' she whispered. 'But what about you? I can't leave you. You too must come with me . . .'

'No, no, that we cannot do. But it is also dangerous for you to go back on your own. We'll try to call your guest house, ask them to send a car for you . . .'

I went outside, wondering what to do. Further down the hill, plumes of grey-black smoke were still billowing from the Balasinghams' house.

At that moment, a police jeep came swiftly along the road. I ran down the hill and hailed it. 'Stop! Please stop!'

The jeep came to a screeching halt at the foot of the drive. A khaki-clad policeman with a baton in his hand got out.

'The mobs are on their way here, converging at the roundabout from Davy Road.' I pointed in that direction. 'Please help us! I have a sick child with me . . . My husband is Tamil . . . They are armed.'

They reversed the jeep and drove off. Perhaps they would hold back the mob for the moment. But tonight, under cover of the darkness, there was little they could do on these deserted roads where curfew is disregarded. I ran back up the hill the Balasinghams' house. The smoke choked me. Policemen stood in the garden with their rifles and batons, while firemen were still trying to douse the last of the embers. They looked utterly weary and exhausted.

I went up to the police officer. 'Help me. I have this English girl who has to get back into town. I cannot keep her with me, we're in too much danger ourselves. Please see that she is taken back to Kandy in the jeep.'

I took the path home. I wanted Deborah to go back safely. That was all. For the moment, worry about our danger had receded. I didn't want her to go through the fear and anxiety that had overcome us.

I took her back to the police officer. 'Goodbye, Deborah,' I said. We held each other close. 'We shall meet one day soon, in England.'

Deborah climbed into the jeep and was driven away.

Now that she was gone, there was nothing left to do but wait. My husband and I played endless guessing games.

'What do we do if they come?'

'Nothing . . .'

'Which door do we escape from?'

'What difference will it make?'

'Where do you think they'll come from? From behind the house, the wilderness behind, or along the front road?'

'Who knows?'

The hours passed. There was nothing we could do but wait. We grew tired and lapsed into silence. That night too passed. Days passed. More nights. We stayed contantly alert, unable to go back to living our normal lives. We tried to do the regular things—shop, cook, clean—but it all required too much effort. The village schoolmaster, the physician and other neighbours came to see how we were getting on. Weeks passed. Months. The papers carried news: committees were sitting, commissions were appointed to investigate the race riots.

I began to sleep again, but there were always fearful

dreams and nightmares. We kept our windows tightly closed. We still felt vulnerable, fearful that we would never be wholly safe again, anywhere. Every sound seemed a threat, even the rustle of a branch, a falling leaf swept by wind, a bird whose shadows swooped past the window pane.

I ventured out into my garden once again but it did not feel the same. I felt a great loss of freedom. Was it because I was married to one of the 'other'? I felt I was cut off from humankind, that I bore an invisible brand which made me experience a sense of fear and shame because of that bonding within my marriage. And where my children were concerned I suffered for that blood bond. Had we done right to make them so vulnerable? Yes, we were all vulnerable. We would now have to rework our strategies of survival. One option would be to be defensive for ever. Open warfare would only end in destruction. Escape? That would be a coward's stance. Exile would make us strangers to ourselves.

I started taking my evening walks by the river again. I know we have find our way back, to start our lives again. Yet each time I gaze at the fathomless depths of the dark waters, I feel I am drowning, drowning . . .

Sanctuary

'PAULUS, ONE OF the leaders of the 1971 insurgency, was ambushed and shot in the jungles of Mahawa in the raid conducted by Inspector Ranasinghe on Sunday evening.'

The words stared up at me from the newspaper I was reading. I had just returned from what turned out to be my last weekend in Mahawa, our coconut plantation in the middle of the jungle. When I was there, I should have realized that I could never come back, or that if I came back, it would not be the same. I had known that Paulus might take refuge in the surrounding jungles. Inspector Ranasinghe, who had dropped in one day while we were there, told us about Paulus. He knew that we were friends, but he did not know how closely he was associated with Mahawa. Paulus had escaped from his guards over a week ago while he was being escorted from one jail to another for security reasons. It was suspected that he was in the area. He knew that the villagers in this area would not betray him. But nor could they protect him forever.

But even if the Inspector had not told me, I should have

known that Paulus was close by. I should have felt his presence in that wilderness. He could go deeper into the virgin forest that any man I knew, among those ancient trees that formed an impenetrable screen round the waterholes where the animals came to drink at night, far beyond the scrubland and thorny thickets. No one else could have penetrated that far. But even such places would soon be found for the jungles were now receding, the trees thinning out where *chenas* had sprung up. Once elephants, bears and sambhur had filled these jungles; and humans were an intrusion. Now it was all changing. Even the police party had penetrated far enough to find Paulus. The sanctity of the jungle was going.

So they got him after all, I thought. That's why Inspector Ranasinghe did not keep his appointment with us that Sunday evening.

'Paulus has already killed about eight people and has a hit list of about twenty more. My name however is not on the hit list,' the Inspector had said that evening. 'His wife is still behind bars. She too was in the insurgency. A crack shot,' he had said with a certain note of admiration. I had thought then that Paulus would not remain alive for much longer. They would hunt him out.

The Inspector was an old student of mine. He had promised to take us to Ridi Bendi Ela that Sunday, but he did not turn up. Instead, he sent one of his constables to say that he was sorry but he had to postpone the trip as he had an important police inquiry to attend to. He had gone to the jungles with a posse of policemen to hunt out Paulus. We had returned to Kandy the next day, unaware of what had taken place.

It had been a weekend of dry and breathless heat. The waterholes were drying up. The *loola* fish had to burrow deep into the mudholes to find water in the parched bed of the *wewa*. The villagers were waiting for the rains. On the estate, the coconut fonds were withering, the nuts were shrunken. That Sunday, we waited all day for the cool of the evening, for the breeze to blow across the paddy fields and for the thickening dusk to shroud the mango trees until it was only the scent of ripening fruit which made known their presence. We sat in the clearing outside the house where all day the men had been piling high the coconuts they gathered, and waited for darkness. Gradually, it cooled until we could feel the heavy dew settling on the flowering bushes, the chill creeping into our bodies and roots of hair. The fireflies shimmered on the lime and jasmine bushes.

But as we sat in the peaceful evening, we had not known that nearby in the jungle Paulus was being hunted down. Probably darkness was the time of greater safety for him, yet it was under cover of darkness that he had been found. In the forest, he would have always had to be on the move. The hunters were never too far away. There would have been no rest for him, his sleep could only have been fitful. It was only have been a matter of time before he was captured. He would have preferred it the way it happened. Paulus would never come out of the jungle alive to be chained and manacled again, to be locked in a cell with no hope of escape. I heard that he had got an ancient shotgun from one of the villagers. Shots had been fired at the police party that was combing the jungle. Once they knew he was there, he could not have escaped. Perhaps he did not want to escape which was why he had fired.

I remember how restless and wakeful I was that night. The night air had seemed alive with the shrill piercing sounds of bird and insect. I could smell the earth, the leaves and that overwhelming fragrance of ripening limes on the cool breeze that blew in through the bars of the window. I had got out of bed and looked out of the window. The sharp linear shadows of trees fell on the cleared area around the house. How stark the contrast of light and dark was! The moonlight had a chill quality to it. I felt cold and fragile. The *ulama's* cry cut sharply through the night. The call of the devil bird is always considered to presage some tragic event. Now I know what that was, but then it felt as if my childhood sanctuary was safe no more, and the home I always thought was there securely for me felt fragile. My sojourn within this sanctuary was only temporary.

The estate had been my uncle's hunting lodge. He named it Mahawattehena, the great chena land. Once it had all been part of the jungle: hoary *mara* and teak trees, tamarind, satinwood, ebony and *halmilla*. The trees had been cleared and cut down for the coconut plantation. A well had been dug, and the water in it was pure and mineral-filled. And my uncle had come down here when he wanted to hunt in the jungle with his weekend guests. When my father inherited it after his brother's death, he turned the estate into a sanctuary.

For us as children, it was the place that all kinds of magical things came from. My father's suitcase when he returned from the estate was always filled with gifts for us.

Packed away with his flutes and his 'jungle kit', as he called
it, there would be ripe wood apples, weaver birds' nests and
the votive *dewale* offerings of woven straw and paddy strands.
And there would be mangoes, crates of them covered with
straw, and roasted *batagoyas* wrapped in *habarala* leaves. He
brought home the jungle with him, and it filled our town
house. The reptile skins, antlers and birds' nests made it look
like a forest shrine. On the walls hung different artefacts:
carved Kandyan swords and Kris knives in their scabbards,
wild boar tusks mounted on wood, and shotguns. He brought
the estate home with him for he always wanted to feel the
presence of the natural world around him. Sacks of new rice
from the fields, coconuts after the first pluck, bunches of
freshly gathered herbs, *karapincha* and *angunakola*. King
coconut oil simmered in clay pots on wood fires with *savendra*
roots to add to its fragrance. Bamboo flutes. Peacock feathers.
All these were even more precious to us because they were
the magical talismans of a father's love for his children.

Later, after the estate became my father's and we started
to go there, we all loved it instinctively. In the evenings, the
oil lamps lit, we would sit listening to the notes of my
father's flute weaving patterns of sound through our minds.
It was at that time that we felt most strongly the deep love
which bound our family together. Why was it that we could
never speak the words that should have been spoken? That
love was always taken for granted, the love of those who
gave of themselves without stint, like a well which never ran
dry even in times of the severest drought.

That Sunday evening, I had taken a walk to the wewa.
For some reason I had taken a path which I had never taken

before. On the way is the teak grove. I had heard that during the 1971 insurgency, deep trenches had been dug there. Insurgents had been rounded up and blindfolded, their hands tied behind their backs. Then they were taken there and shot, their bodies plummeting into the freshly dug trenches. 'It's à haunted place. We never pass that way after dark. We hear the wailing cries of the dying. Their spirits are restless,' Nanda the housekeeper told me. She came from Kolabissa, a faraway village in the hills of Kandy. None of the villagers would take that path, and I too had always avoided it.

As I walked down that path that evening, I felt a chill touch my limbs. Where the trenches had been was now covered with thorny spikes of grass. It was in shadow, the dark foliage of the teak trees overhanging it. Unclaimed graves, the anonymous dead. As I walked by them, I should have thought of Paulus, I should have felt that he was somewhere out there, watching, waiting for his own death.

I felt relieved when I reached the bund of the wewa. I would take the memory of that peaceful moment back with me to Kandy. And along with that memory, all the other memories from my childhood that came flooding back as I sat by the wewa that evening. The women, long since dead and gone, would bathe there in the still evening hours. The pink and white *nelun* flowers with their elegant green leaves and stalks would tremble and move as they plunged their bodies into the water. It was a silent world, they would be intent on what they were doing, away from their menfolk and the tasks that kept them busy all day—cooking, gathering firewood, washing clothes and working in the fields. Their sleek, wet hair covered their shoulders. Their pots bobbed up and down. There was never much water in the wewa but it was always full of nelun flowers. It was as if a net of green, pink and white had looped up the blue water, holding the women in thrall. It was a world of enchantment. Even today, the women still reserve the twilight hours for themselves.

Along the bund were laden wood apple trees. Cattle wandered under them. Three bullocks ran out of one of the compounds and onto the path. A tall, gaunt woman pursued them and herded them back with her stick. This was the true heart of the land where the people of the soil had lived for centuries. I was a stranger among them, but because this was their land where they belonged, it was easy for them to accept me as one who would merely come and go. I would take nothing from them, except the magical stories I had heard from the ancient ones in the village. This was their land, and had been for generations. All they wanted was to hold on to what they had, as it was, not to extend it or stretch the boundaries.

Why was everything about that last holiday in Mahawa so firmly etched in my memory? Was there some presaging that I would never return to that house with its ancient tiles and walls adorned with glittering reptile skins, weaver birds' nests, antlers and woven paddy strands? And filled with family photographs, of my great-grandparents with their offspring, all dressed in Victorian clothes, and with books and photograph albums. Did I imagine that I would never again drink the water from the well which my father flavoured with sassaparilla, which not only made it sweet to the palate but also purified the blood and cooled the body?

There are rootless people and drifters like me who set out on haphazard, unplanned journeys. We do this to counter the terrible dissonances of the voices that crowd about our ears. We need to create a magical world into which we can escape. So our journeys are without maps, with only the signposts of memory left by past travellers who have since vanished into the thorny thickets and leafy canopies of the jungles. This world which we want to find is a timeless one. You accept everything as it is: the landscape, the water, the cries of birds, the taste of fruit. You name things in a language of your own devising. Thought, textures, odours, all intermingle. Some such travellers had come to the jungle before me to find their own peace. My father was one of them. From him I learned to seek out such a sanctuary, where one could feel the peace within.

As long as my father was alive, this was his sanctuary. He taught me the language of birds. We would stand among the lime bushes and the jasmines, and imitate their calls, and the birds would come flocking. Were we trying out new identities? Trying to become part of nature, or at least use nature as a protective camouflage?

The leaves and earth were always fragrant with the wild creatures that dwelt in them. 'Don't go into the coconut grove after dark,' my mother would warn me. In the deep ditch just outside the estate, steeped in moisture and proliferting with life, flourished the secret life of reptile and lizards. The roots of the enormous gnarled trees reached deep into the innermost sources of that growing.

When I had first come to the estate as a child, the jungle had been dense, thickly crowded with closely growing trees.

Now the jungle seemed to be moving further and further away from the boundaries of the estate. Iguanas once used to come freely into the garden and at night, we could hear jackals close by. The crocodiles which had lived in the wewas were now gone. My father had once seen an enormous coiled python with antlers protruding from its mouth by the wewa. As he was looking at it, a huge hawk had swooped down from the sky and carried it off. The python had been too heavy and sluggish to move away from its claws.

I thought of my father who was no longer alive. I missed his presence every moment. Everytime I came here, I made it a point to meet the old people from the village who still remembered him. Gillan who had looked after the estate for him was also long since dead. His tomb was in the paddy field beside the coconut grove. He had asked to be buried there. He wanted to be close to the gods of the village for whom he had carried out the ancient rituals after the harvesting of the paddy.

Did I want to find a home here, in this land surrounded by jungle? The land is often parched with drought, when the rains fail or when the wewas run dry. I have no place of my own to belong to. I am one of the disinherited city-dwellers, without land of my own, moving from place to place and settling in as best I could in houses that were only temporary abodes. Maybe that is why this place represented such a sanctuary to me, because of the permanence I saw in the lives around me. For Sena, for Jaya, for Semasinghe Mudiyanse and for all the others I knew in the nearby villages, there was a sense of sweetness and security that in the knowledge that they belonged so completely to the land which no one would ever take away from them, where their forefathers had lived before them. That was the kind of permanence and security that I could never imagine.

When I was growing up, a teenager, every school holiday meant coming down to the estate. The train journey was long, we had to change trains at one point. I remember our excitement growing as the landscape changed outside the window. Flat land, scrub, jungle; the air dry but still. When we arrived at Mahawa station, we would take a rickety old taxi to the estate. There would be flat plains all around, wewas thick with lilies, paddy fields and dark groves of tamarind and mango. Occasionally, we would drive down from the city, scattering herds of cattle wandering quietly along the road. Even as children, as soon as we arrived at the estate, we would feel this suspension of time, even an absence of time. We felt we would be like this forever, and never grow up, living in this magical world, always protected by my mother and my father.

The first thing I would do when I arrived at the estate was run to the well and peer into its depths. I would draw up buckets of cold water and splash them on my body. Our well never ran dry, even in times of drought. The hot days had the flavour of wild sassaparilla. And in the evening, watching the fireflies twinkling on the lime bushes, I would know my vacation had truly begun.

When we were young, the household was run by Gillanhamy and his wife Menike. Later on, we took Lily there, all the way from Kandy, to cook for us. Gillan cultivated his own paddy fields as well as ours. The kitchen was some distance from the house, beside a strip of paddy. From there,

64

the fields stretched flatly for miles. On the other side of the house was the jungle.

We ate country food: *kurakkan* ground on flat stones, rotis baked on the iron *kabala*, with a mixture of coconut, sliced red onions and green chillies. For breakfast, we would have *kiribath*. The brown rice was from our fields, the milk in which it was cooked came from the coconuts that hung in clusters from the trees in the garden. The bitter angunakola, which we ate finely sliced, sharp with lime and salt, and the tender pumpkin and pumpkin leaves grew in our garden. We caught loola fish in the wewa and brought them home to cook. I would go to the kitchen to watch Gillan cleaning the fish with wood ash. My father brought home wild pigeon and jungle fowl, which was marinated with pepper, salt, turmeric and lime, and baked in earthenware *chatties*. Menike would bring us honey-sweet *vein thalapa*, shaped liked diamonds. During the mango season, gunny sacks full of fruit were carefully handpicked. The tiny *mi-amba* were left on the trees for the squirrels and the marauding bats. From the wewa, baskets of lotus tubers were brought home. They were covered with dark, hairy sheaths. After they were boiled in clay pots set on the wood fire, the sheaths were peeled off. The flesh was white and smooth, and tasted nutty.

The heat was always overwhelming during the day, and we were thirsty all the time. Our favourite drink was coconut water. The golden clusters of *thambili* were carefully lowered on ropes from the coconut tree, and we drank from the brimming glass jugs which were constantly replenished. The coconut water was sweet in itself but we always flavoured it with lime and stirred in a few grains of sugar. The scooped-out coconut kernel, milky white, floated on the surface like scraps of cloud.

Safe. That is what I always felt here, safe. The secret life of the jungle would never hurt me. From the large outer room, one could see three sides of the estate over the half-walls. The inner room, where we slept with our mother, was close to the jungle. Lying in bed, I could hear the whirr of the crickets and the lonely cry of the jackal. The smells of the jungle wafted in on the cool night breeze. I felt I was sleeping in the jungle itself. The wild creatures would constantly wander into the estate fearlessly, making us aware of their nearness. If we heard gunshot then, it meant that there were hunters in search of game.

All day we heard the sounds of birds. I loved the haunting call of the white crane. My father could identify each call. There were many books on birds in the house with vivid colour plates, written by planters or their wives. The ones I liked best were by Cecily Lushington. The nest of the weaver bird that hung empty on the wall was my favourite plaything. I loved to explore the intricate fleecy maze of tunnels and passages, lined with the softest jungle cotton, that lay within the fine mesh of the surface of the nest.

One day a fawn wandered into the estate. Perhaps a hunter had shot its mother. It stayed on, grew tame and nibbled leaves from our hands. There were many serpents on the estate, a few of them were deadly. My father taught us to identify them by their markings. He once found a mapila curled under his mattress.

My father slept under a mosquito net in the outer room,

beside the half-wall, so that he could feel the cool night breeze. He loved going for solitary walks in the jungle, swinging his stout walking stick and listening to birdcalls. He trod gently so that the dried leaves would not rustle as he wandered through the jungle track. And so wild hares would dart across his path, iguanas wander out of thickets to peer at him, and deer grazing in secluded glades would not run away at his approach. There were ruins of ancient buildings in the jungle which my father discovered, scattered stone pillars belonging to past civilizations.

In the evenings as dusk fell and the fragrance from the jasmine bushes wafted into the house, my father would play his flute, its tones mellowed by time and by his sensitive touch. Listening to him, I always felt that I was wandering alone through the forest, invisible to the watching eyes of both spirits and animals. I followed the melody weaving a path through the trees, picking up echoes from the rustle of leaves, the cries of birds, and the whirring of myriads of unknown, unseen insects—all making up the music of the forest. I became part of a secret and magical world where there was no guilt or fear, where there were no threats. It was of no importance that there was no predictable destination.

And Paulus was a part of that magical world. We had been friends since we were children, and because he had no family to spend his vacations with, my parents had always brought him along with us. And though over the years, our paths had separated, he had moved into the world of political activism and I had retreated to my books, our bonds had never weakened for we shared memories of this enchanted childhood world.

Somewhere over the years, I lost that music. It was not just when the flute was put away after my father's death and I listened to the birds alone. I felt it most strongly that evening as I wandered back from the wewa. I had an enormous sense of desolation, a realization that the music of the forest was lost forever. And at that time, I had no idea that this was a premonition of Paulus' death.

Whenever I went down to the estate, I made it a point to visit Semasinghe Mudiyanse. He was Gillan's brother and one of the few people left from my childhood. That Sunday afternoon, I had gone to see him. His white hair, streaked with grey, was neatly combed back, strand by strand, and knotted into a smooth *konde*. He was revered in the village for his wisdom and because he was supposed to possess magical powers. His history was more important than mine would ever be. He had chosen to live close to the truth of earth and nature. Everything that grew out of that fertile soil helped to nurture him. His forefathers had their fields and chenas for generation after generation in this village, and Semasinghe, his sons and their children would inherit this land. The land itself was instinct with the sounds and the voices of the ancient village and the jungle. It seemed to me that this was where the spirit was released of its constraints and found true freedom. These voices were different from those in the missionary school where I had studied; those seemed to belong to characters in a world of fiction.

Semasinghe walked back home with me, tapping his stick on the paddy field. He was almost blind. His voice was like that of the ancient bard. When we were children, he would come to visit my father and sit on the veranda, and tell us stories of his life and childhood. Semasinghe's murmurous voice drifting through the heat shimmering in the air was another of the constants of my childhood. He would describe his childhood as if he were relating an ancient folk tale. One of my favourite stories was the story of his hair.

'My hair was long and thick, black and heavy,' he would begin. 'If I left it untied, it reached to my knees so I had to knot it up. There was this very special *chandrakanthi* oil which my father made for my hair. It was full of herbs: *mukunewenna, keketiya* which grew near the wewa, *kikirindiya* from by the paddy fields, and *vetakeiyawa* roots. These herbs were chopped up, pounded in the wooden mortar, and soaked in water for three days. Then the juices were squeezed out and added to bottles of goat's milk. The mixture was heated and other things added to it—*sarakku, valmi, kothamalli,* a variety of roots and seeds, and finely-ground *kaipu*. It was boiled down till it was thick. Different oils were added— ghee, sesame and castor oils. It was through instinct that you knew when it was done, when you felt the texture of the herb mixture between your fingers.

'My hair was so long that only my father could tie it up for me. One day, at school, I was playing and my hair came untied and flowed down my back. I couldn't knot it up by myself, so I went up to one of my brothers and said, Loku aiya, please tie up my hair for me. When I went home that day, my father made me an ebony *koora* to keep my konde in place, and it never came untied again.

'Once, when I was very young, my father had decided

that it was time to cut my hair. My mother had gone to fetch water. My father consulted my horoscope and found the auspicious time. Just as he was going to start cutting, my mother returned. She took me away at once. My hair was never cut after that.'

He would tell us stories about his education: 'My father wanted us to be educted. I studied up to the seventh grade in school. We had about a hundred buffaloes. My father milked them himself. We would make the milk into curd and sell it. But then one day *vasangatha*, that is rinderpest, broke out in Polpitigama, a nearby village. Baapa, my uncle, told us to bring our buffaloes to where he lived, which was further away from Polpitigama. But his buffaloes too got sick, and about a week later, so did ours. They began to die off rapidly, about seven a day. All we could do was to dig up the earth near the Mahawewa and bury them. We buried about a hundred of them. Only one cow and a buffalo were left.'

Or about village rituals: 'After I left school, I worked on my father's fields and then later, on my own. Before we first ploughed a field, we would take a coconut and place it on a a wooden post in the middle of the *nyera*, the earth ridge between the fields. There are harvest rituals too. Before we threshed the grain, we took milk from the first coconut of the season and boiled it on the *kamatha*, the threshing floor. When we made kiribath with the new rice, we first served it to the gods before we ate. Each god—Vishnu, Kataragamdeviyo, Siddha Sat Pattini Maniya, Kambili devata, Kadawara devata, Gam devata, Kinnara devata—had his own *kehel gottuwa*, made of plaited banana leaf, into which

70

the kiribath was ladled. The rest we would distribute among the people, along with betel and arecanut *panduru*, the offerings to repay our vows, while we sang kavi verses of invocation and beat on the *udekki* drums.'

But the story he told me that Sunday was different from all the other stories, for it was a story of hatred. It was the story of the one time he had left the village for more than a few days, and the only long journey he had ever undertaken. This was many years ago. The *vedemahataya*, the ayurvedic physician, had hired him to make use of his special powers to destroy his enemy.

'It was dawn when we set out. I recited the mantras I had learnt from my *gurunanse* and ate the food prescribed before such rites are performed. There was meat and fish, with a variety of grains—*puluthu*, mung, *thala* and paddy. We went by train to the south. It was a long, long journey. We didn't know who the enemy was, but we knew where we could find him.

'We reached that place and went to the house of the woman who read the *anjanan eliya* through which she made her predictions. She told us who the enemy was. I prepared the *dehi tinduwa*. I arranged twenty-four betel leaves like petals, and limes and sliced arecanut. I don't remember precisely what I did. There were many prayers and incantations, and as I recited them, I slipped more and more into a trance-like state. I remember I had to slash the throat of a cock. I remember swallowing fire and dancing in a trance. When I had finished, the *gotta* of woven reed with all the flesh, fish and grains over which I uttered my spells and incantations was thrown on the land of the enemy. The whole ritual took three days. We rested for a few days and then we prepared for our return journey. Meanwhile the house of the vedamahataya's enemy caught fire and was burnt to the ground.'

But Semasinghe, the vedamahataya's enemy was not your enemy, I thought. Why did you do it? You used your power to destroy another man. I could not imagine doing that. I could not imagine anyone in my family doing anything like that, however much pain or suffering someone had caused us.

After Semasinghe had left, I continued to think of him. Why did he have to tell me this story? It seemed so completely at variance with that other life—the fertility rites, the forest, the abundance of grain and fruit that the earth yielded, the protective deities who cared for the village—with which I had always associated him. Even his hair was nourished by the seeds and roots that came from the earth. Looking at Semasinghe, I had always seen in my imagination the land as it had once been—the earth green, the jungles teeming with animals, the benevolent gods and the goddesses who were part of the cycle of cultivation and harvesting, the water holes full as the monsoons came at the ordained time.

But all that was changing. Soon the herbs that were culled for the magical chandrakanthi oil would be difficult to find. The land was wounded with violence and drought. The trees were sparse. The fugitives would not find sanctuary much longer within the jungle.

So perhaps that was why Semasinghe was willing to destroy a friend's enemy. He believed in his powers. He also believed that good and evil that existed side by side, and the latter had to be destroyed. He accepted their inevitability. After all, as he was so close to the earth, he could see its corruption. He perhaps felt that he had destroyed some small part of the evil that threatened to overcome the land.

He could see that the land was still indestructible. The roots stretched deep beneath the earth. There were hidden pools of water. That water tasted of the forest with the leaves that fell from overhanging branches. Fruit and berries and seeds reposed at the bottom of those rock pools. Some of those pools never dried up.

Semasinghe would never leave this land. It was his home, he would live and die here. He knew of no other life beyond his home in the jungle. Which is why he was willing to fight the enemy within it. For Paulus, the jungle was only a temporary refuge. To leave it would be death. For me too, the sanctuary was part of the illusion of safety. I wanted to vanish into that jungle and be forgotten but nothing here in reality belonged to me. I was a visitor, and yet this place had given me an insight into the wisdom and knowledge of these people for whom there was no conflict, no anger, no sense of loss and displacement. Yet the revolution had reached them. The young people had come out to share in that newly-found ideology, to change this world of their forefathers. They had been captured, taken away, their youth buried in the freshly-dug trenches of the teak grove, anonymous graves from which their identities would never be recovered.

What was lacking in my own life? Why did I have this rootlessness, this sense of displacement? Was it the hybridity of my birth that constantly created this dichotomy within me? I was always searching for that sanctuary of perfect peace which I could never find. I know that would not happen easily. There was evil to be faced and destroyed.

I was secure here, safe, but I knew it would not be for ever. I was like the grub within the mango, living within the seed, feeding on the ripe, golden-nectared flesh. Living for so brief, so transitory a time.

Soon the fugitive would need to go far into the jungle for shelter. The hunters would follow. The predators would always be there. The reptiles watch and wait. The deer, alert and wide-eyed in the glades, the leopard in its lair, they all wait. There would be more sounds, echoes of gunshot, over and over again. The music of my father's flutes were lost forever, never to be heard again.

I had finally to accept the severance from that safe place. A place that I always thought of as sanctuary, a country that had for me more than one name or no name at all, the world of childhood. I realized, as I held that newspaper in my hand, that part of the reason why I longed to go back was to leave the terrors of an unpredictable future. We all have dreams that we will find a magical place to belong to, where no one would discover us. No one would care to even know your name, a name that would mean nothing here in this trackless way into the very depths of the jungle where you could walk as far as you wanted. Where a uniform darkness engulfed you.

The Crossing

I

I BEGAN MY journey at the dead of night, in pitch darkness, from Nallur where my home is. I travel from the south to the north of the island quite frequently. I like to come home as often as I can, to see my father and my younger sister, my only sister. I'm studying for my engineering degree in the south. The only people who matter to me live in the peninsula. I have to assure myself of their safety. And I know that they long to see me too; my visits are all they have to look forward to in their monotonous lives.

To reach the mainland from the peninsula, one had to cross the lagoon in a motor boat or a fishing vallam. We can no longer take the old routes for it is a time of war. But the crossing is now growing familiar to me, for I have made this journey many times.

The journey is difficult, and there are many hazards along the way. There are innumerable checkpoints. Part of it is through a desert no-man's land, which I have named the

'Dead Zone'. For part of the way, the only transport one can get is in an overcrowded tractor. And then there is the crossing itself. There are no quays where one embarks or disembarks from the boat. We have to wade out into the water until it is waist-high, or sometimes even shoulder-high.

The peninsula is now officially divided from the south. A de facto state exists there, under the rule of the most powerful militant group, the Liberation Tigers of Tamil Eelam. They are fighting for a separate state for our people. The war has been going on for several decades now; a never-ending war which has resulted in the displacement of thousands belonging to the different ethnic communities in the island. Many people call them fascists.

The journey out of the peninsula costs thousands of rupees. Guarantees are needed, someone has to stand surety for you when you leave the peninsula. The militants are informed of all our movements, and they exact their tolls and taxes too. Gold sovereigns. Yet nothing deters the traveller. Children studying, working, living in the south return to visit their parents. Parents leave the north to see their children in the south. The same imperatives exist, which have always existed. War does not change people's needs. It's only the routes and means that have changed.

It is not only the journeys which have changed for us. There's an army camp in the peninsula, at Palaly. It is like a separate world. It must seem like an alien world for them too. They face constant attacks from the militants, hemmed in within that camp. Their supplies are flown in by helicopter and cargo planes, or carried in by boat. Everything they need has to come from across the waters.

In the peninsula, people go about their business as best they can. They are cut off from the south, and from the rest of the world as well. They experience many hardships: embargoes, no electricity, no petrol. They have learnt to manage with natural light, and after dark, with oil lamps. But even the oil is precious. They don't see any newspapers from the south. Letters have to be carried by friends, relatives or the ICRC. Books too. There are no books to be had any more. The famous library in the town of Jaffna was burned down a long time ago. Invasions. Military occupations.

I knew, without really thinking about it, that I couldn't spend the rest of my life here. I was young. I had no intention of being a martyr to the cause. It was not that I was a traitor, or that I had no sense of loyalty towards my people. I was just not prepared for great sacrifices, for showing my valour on the battlefield, for biting on the cyanide capsule. I have responsibilities, things to do. Once I get my engineering degree, I will join my brother in Switzerland. Hundreds of thousands of my people are scattered all over the world: asylum seekers, political refugees. I want to arrange a marriage for my sister with someone who lives abroad. My father has aged beyond his years after my mother's early death, it's too much for him to plan my sister's wedding by himself. He's already given up on life . . .

It's always difficult to say goodbye to the two of them when I leave home. But it has to be done. I know I have work to do which I must finish. All they can do is wait for my next visit. The most painful part for them is not to be sure, never to be sure, when they will see me again, to live with that uncertainty when they are alone, as darkness descends early on the land and they light the small brass oil lamp that will be their beacon.

Every time as I leave, my father and sister wait at the doorway. As I walk away, I can sense these silent watchers, reluctant to go indoors until they know that my figure has vanished completely out of sight. When the shadows swallow me up, they bolt and bar the doors and return to the silence and the darkness, each deeply absorbed in his own thoughts. But still the peninsula is home to them. My father will never be happy in any other part of the island, nor in any other part of the peninsula except Nallur. His history and the history of his ancestors lie here.

My father was once a wealthy businessman, dealing in gold. He had many craftsmen working for him, who created traditional jewellery for every occasion: births and comings of age, betrothals and weddings. All that had to be given up. We are now supported by my brother who has sought political asylum in Switzerland. My sister weeps when she sees me. She feels so insecure, living alone with only my father. He is now her responsibility. My mother died when she was in her early forties. She never recovered from an attack of asthma. The drugs and hospital treatment she needed were not available.

When I am home, my father and sister know some measure of happiness. I study even when I come to the peninsula. What else is there to do? I have learnt to make use of every bit of natural light in order to conserve the small amount of kerosene oil for our one lamp. My sister cooks what she thinks I like, and we share our simple meals by the light of the lamp. There hasn't been electricity in the peninsula for some years now. We use every bit of available light, rise at dawn, sleep early. We use the lamp sparingly, when we eat and to find our way about the house. Although by now, as we become used to wandering in the dark, each household object has become a familiar landmark

When will we see each other again? The question is never asked, but it is engraved in our minds. Yet they are happy that I am living in the hills. The hill capital in the interior of the island is safer than Colombo. In Colombo, there is perpetual ethnic and racial conflict between the majority community and the ethnic 'other', the minority Tamils. Every day there are conflagrations, bomb blasts, assassinations and suicide bombers. There have been thousands of deaths of innocent civilians of all communities. There are many harrowing tales of arrests, detention camps, torture and interrogation. Bodies have been fished out of the waterways. And nowadays there are new urban legends: people strangled with plastic handcuffs, starved and tortured to death in city hideouts. History goes backwards and forwards. The whole city is caught up in that terrible feeling of insecurity. When will the next bomb go off and where? Where will the suicide bomber choose to strike? Whose body will be shattered in the explosion?

Life in the universities is disrupted too: strikes, lectures and examinations postponed, classes disrupted, the university closed. Yet in the university, we are not separated by our racial identities. We live together in the halls of residence, attend the same lectures, take the same examinations, gain the same qualifications. We are not seen as 'the enemy', I am not made to feel an outsider. So for me, the journey from north to south is from one life to another, but both are mine. I belong in both places. Or in neither. But the difficulty of the journey effectively marks the transition between the two.

I take the minibus to Kilaly, from where the boat leaves at midnight. When we reach there and climb out of the bus, other travellers emerge from the shadows. There are quite a number of us setting out for the south tonight, men, women, a few children.

The tide is high tonight. We prepare to wade into the water. My possessions are all in a urea bag, which is now soaking wet. We are surrounded by darkness and the sound of lapping water. Waves are dangerous, they lull the senses. There is no moon tonight. This is good; it helps to avoid detection. The children are carried on the shoulders of the adults. There is not a murmur from any of them, they are absorbed in this strange midnight adventure.

A motor boat awaits us, tossing and rocking in the high tide. There is a rapid headcount. There are fourteen of us, all ordinary people with duties and obligations, leaving the peninsula. Temporarily? Who knows? Sometime the guerillas make the crossing in these boats too. Not this time. At least not that I can tell.

All of us are intent on a single purpose. There is a strange comfort in the silent presence of bodies all around, all focused on the same thing. We each wait politely for our turn to clamber into the boat. Getting in is not easy. You have to grip the side of the rocking boat with one hand, toss in your possessions with the other, and then swing yourself up and clamber in. Thankfully, there are many helping hands in the boat.

We settle ourselves in. 'Anybody left out?' Everyone talks in whispers.

'Yes, everybody is in.'

There is only the sound of breathing, laboured and agonized, and a few sighs. But there is no talking, apart from murmurs from parents soothing young children. Many have made the journey before, and know what it entails.

We are all bound on different missions. But unlike other journeys, we do not exchange notes or share life stories. The strange intimacy that the freedom of normal journeys creates, where one can talk to strangers about very personal things secure in the knowledge that they will never meet again, never happens here. There are no discussions at all, and certainly nothing of a personal nature. Questions like, 'Which part of the peninsula do you come from? Which island? Which village? Do you know such-and-such?' remain unasked. We look at one another in the darkness and try to imagine the life stories. Has he got sons or daughters abroad? Is she married or widowed? Has he lost any of his children in the conflict? Would he come back to the north or settle down in the south? Has he sold his house and property or did he have to give over the house to the militants? Anyone standing surety for him in the north? Medical treatment? Departure to other countries? Unasked questions. Unanswered questions. We all become meditative; this is a time for introspection.

Huddled bodies take up whatever cramped positions they can in the crowded boat. An old man wheezes. I can feel the tremors of the other chilled bodies touching mine.

The engine of our motor boat is not in the best condition. As we gather speed, the boat rocks from side to side.

I think of my conversations with Ananda, my roommate in the university. He is a devout Buddhist, and he has told me about the samsaric ocean, the ocean of sorrows that man has to build a raft and cross during his life's journey. Ananda interprets this as the human form that the Buddha took during his journey to enlightenment. After the journey is over, man leaves behind the raft, and so too we should leave behind hatred, attachment and other human weaknesses. But Ananda has never made this crossing. I wonder what he would have thought of it.

It is futile to try to keep track of time passing. I can't distinguish any object in the darkness. There are only sounds and movements, my other senses are sharpened because I can't see. The heaving of the boat, the chugging of the motor. The boat is very overloaded. Hope it's seaworthy, I think. There is a high wind tonight. The waves rise as the boat cuts a swathe through the waters. We are all engulfed in spray, drenched to the skin. We shiver, lips and skin crinkle and pucker. I touch my face, it is damp and chill: A slight cough, quickly stifled, echoes from out of the shadows at the other end.

Despite our physical closeness, we are detached from one another. We do not know each other's stories, we do not really want to know. Knowledge can be dangerous, and besides it creates bonds. We each have our individual missions which we must accomplish. We have all learnt to be survivors. I am fierce about protecting my books and lecture notes within their files in the urea bag. They are crucial for what

I have to do.

Suddenly a sliver of moon appears from behind the dark clouds and lays a white wing across them. For a moment I'm able to see the faces of some of my fellow travellers who are sitting close to me. Beside me is a middle-aged woman. Perhaps she is journeying to see a son or a daughter. All the faces I can see have one common expression, resolutely devoid of individuality or emotion. All of us have instinctively worn uniformly drab or grey garments. Anonymity is the garment we all want to wear. We are anonymous travellers, going into a greater anonymity.

The middle-aged woman is peering intently at my urea bag. This is a symbol of both the student and the terrorist. The former would be also wearing a cyanide capsule around the neck, and carrying an AK-47. Tonight, no one seems to be carrying a weapon. But one never knows. It would not be safe to flaunt it even among one's own people. There are always informers.

One constant fear is that we will be mistaken for terrorists. When huge explosions take place and the innocent are buried beneath the debris, their bodies charred so badly that sometimes only the ashes remain, we all feel the guilt. It is as if we had committed the act, for are we not identified with the enemy?

The movement of the boat is irregular. The ancient motor seems to be in need of repair. A part of my mind is constantly alert for other sounds. We all look up from time to time at the sky. Helicopters may suddenly appear. We're an easy target, bobbing in an open stretch of water with no possibility of hiding or escape. The security forces are well aware that the guerillas make the crossing too. So suspicious helicopters or naval vessels may fire on us, thinking us to be militants. At the same time, we could be attacked by the militants and the Sea Tigers too. We are at risk from both sides.

At the moment, for all our anonymity and strangeness, we are all concerned with the same thing. There is a total and absolute preoccupation with our own survival. We are also aware that our survival can only be as a group, so we are desperately concerned about the welfare of all our fellow travellers. A strange sensation, this concern for people we have never met before and would never see again. But either we all make the crossing, or none of us do. Perhaps we may this time. Fate. Destiny. Life. Death. I think about all these words as I sit huddled in the boat.

Sometimes I dream of a man in a black mask, clad in a black diving suit. He leaps into our boat from another vessel and slashes our throats with a sharp knife. Death at sea. Splashes as the bodies are tossed into the water. An empty boat left bobbing on the waves. Sometimes I dream of death on land too. In the jungles, in the border villages. Hacked to death. Shot. Mass graves. Burnt houses. Ashes. The groans of the dead and dying fill my mind. Bodies laid out like dead fish.

I turn my mind resolutely to life on the campus, the life that I am going back to, and think of conversations with my friends in the hall of residence. Some of the Sinhala students are radicals. They try to understand the reasons for this conflict, and to see our point of view. What shocks them are the massacres in the remote border villages.

'Innocent people, no, *machan*? Women and children too. Hacking. Shooting. Burning their huts. Poor people, no?' Sandun observes.

'Reprisal killings too,' I interject.

'And the suicide bombers? The cyanide capsules?' Ananda asks.

'That's because they are fighting for a cause they believe in. Not because they are unemployed, there are no chances for a better life,' Sandun persists. Not that he doesn't think patriotism comes into it. He tells us stories of how before the soldiers go on their forays, they are exhorted by their commanders, reminded that they are the heroes of the hour, fighting to protect the motherland. Which is why Sandun finds me a contradiction. 'Your boys are fighting for a separate homeland in the north and east, yet you come and live among us in the south . . .'

We are surrounded by theories. They grow as thick as trees around us, and every day new saplings sprout up among the hoary old veterans. One of the most widely-held theories is that the island will become a vassal of the subcontinent. Most of my fellow students are highly politicized. They spend hours discussing this and other theories.

Ananda is an exception to this. But even he is not sure that his engineering studies are what interest him. Sometimes he says he wants to give it all up and become a *bhikku*.

On our campus, normal student activities like ragging become extreme forms of torture. Some see this as a form of testing. They say that the radical political parties use campus ragging as a means to select recruits for their movement.

Those who do not break under the physical and mental degradation and abasement they're subjected to are ideal for their cause. Strange though, even our people from the north do not abstain from ragging. Sometimes they are even more brutal in their methods. Power, that's how I see it. It gives some people pleasure to see others cringe beneath the whip.

I think about the room that I share with Ananda in the hall of residence. It is a sacred space for us. We do not drag into it the cumbersome baggage of identity, of what we were and what we have been through. Each of us have had our own struggles.

They tell me stories of what took place in the south before I entered the campus. I listen to their whisperings about the disappearances during the insurrection, the arrests, the detention camps, the torture and the killings. Beating to death with iron rods, the tyre burnings. The remains of many mutilated bodies have been exhumed from mass graves, reduced to shreds of cloth, bones and skulls. Many of the witnesses are still alive. Question. Answer. The aftermath. An eye for an eye. A tooth for a tooth.

I listen to all the stories which they tell me. We don't belong to different camps here. But they're curious about our comings and goings. The north is a closed world to them. The terrain is only familiar to armies of occupation. Only they know the different routes that we take on our journeys.

'Machan, how do you get across? You cross the lagoon, no?' Sandun asks.

'Fishing boats, motor boats . . .' I don't disclose too much even to them

'Tigers also come to the south, no? All these suicide

bombers? And you, how did you manage to keep out of the movement . . . they come to the schools to recruit their cadres, don't they?' Sandun is always the most persistent questioner. Sometimes I feel caged. When there is too much interrogation.

Ananda usually comes to the rescue. 'When you come to the south, we see you as another student. Not as a Tiger. You're like the man who builds a raft to cross the sea of *samsara*,' he says.

'Ah, *bana* preaching!' Sandun lolls on the bed, relaxed, barebodied, clad in his sarong, drinking a mug of plain tea. Sandun's eldest brother was arrested. He disappeared during the uprising of 1989. His mother still believes he may be alive somewhere and will return home one day. Perhaps she is right, perhaps he is still locked away in an underground prison.

Ananda has not been deterred by the interruption. 'The man builds his own raft. Uses grass, branches and leaves. Gets across. But he's got to leave it behind once he has crossed from this shore to that. From danger to safety. He can't carry the raft on his shoulders. Can't get too attached to it. He has to accept change, leave all hatred behind . . .'

That's the way Ananda sees it. Or else he could not accept me. He has to see me as one who has left all hatred behind, not as an enemy living among them. He doesn't hate me. Nor do I see him as the enemy. I don't know what I am any more. Only that within myself I feel deeply divided.

The chugging of the motor boat slows down. We are close to Alangkerni, where we disembark. Once more we have to step into the water, this time to wade to the shore.

I help the woman who was sitting next to me. Her teeth are chattering with cold, her wet clothes cling to her body. The landscape here is only sand, and more sand. Here and there in the shadows are scattered groups, resting for a while before the next lap of the journey, waiting resignedly for the tractor to arrive. The crossing is but one part.

We bide our time. The woman seems to have vanished into a kovil that I can see in the distance. We will all meet later in the tractor. Somtimes there are as many as fifty people in it, all wet to the skin. There is no other way to across this sandy waste. The tractor takes us to Omanthai, a fifteen-minute journey. From there, we have to walk to Vavuniya, a three-kilometre walk. There are checkpoints to be gone through along the way. Militants on one side, security forces on the other. Once we reach Vavuniya, we can take a bus or train to continue on our way. It is also only in Vavuniya that we can get food or drink.

But now we are still in the wasteland, in this vast expanse of sand, without hope of oasis, or even the delusion of a mirage. No vegetation to give any indication of life, not even a solitary cactus. Even that would be some kind of landmark, give hope to the lost and solitary traveller. In this emptiness, there is a temptation to give in, to stop and bury yourself in the timeless sand. Let the sand cover you, your eyes, sink into a hollow, in eternal sleep . . .

But no, the journey must continue. I do not know what impediments I am still to encounter on the way but first of all I've got to leave all hatred behind. The boat in which I have travelled has served its turn. I have used it, as Ananda said, to cross the samsaric ocean of life. But have I left behind the negative emotions, the feelings of enmity, which he spoke of? I have yet to fulfill my obligations towards those among whom I now live, in the south. We've got to listen to each other's grievances, we have to understand each other.

For the moment, however, I can only think mechanically in terms of movement—minibus, boat, tractor, minibus—and of the impediments on the way. The checkpoints where I may be stopped, questioned; checkpoints where the eyes of strangers open flaps in my mind and body, and peer into the complex nerve structure within me. Just thinking about it, fear makes the blood in my veins grow sluggish, forming a turgid pool.

Memory wakes again as I wait in that wasteland. My sister's tear-stained face in the faint glimmer of an uncertain and wavering flame, shadowed grotesquely; the deep furrows etched like some archaic script on my father's sagging brow, waiting for me to decipher it. An old man and a young girl sharing a life, half of which is spent in darkness. That is not the home I remember. Where is home, then, the true home, except in memory? Our homes one day will be empty of even our shadows.

The stretch of water I have crossed marks the formal separation of my two lives. I cannot renounce either of them. I travel with my double identity, but as I journey south, I feel myself slipping into the one which enables me to live at peace with the others at the university. We share the same lineaments. How can I say that they are not of my kind? Yet we are divided, our oneness cracking under the weight of history.

I rub my skin absent-mindedly. It still hurts where the

salt of the sea water has stung those small bruises, scatches and tears which one always acquires on the boat journey. The pain somehow makes the senses more alert.

What if bridges spanned that expanse of water? As a student of engineering, I always construct things in my imagination. I have been taught how to construct things that will endure, that are meant to endure despite the power of the elemnts lashing against them. But will they survive the war? I dream of constructing roads that lead directly to destinations, roads that will make such journeys easier for all those who want to travel—the student, the pilgrim, the soldier, the militant, the guerilla, the terrorist. I see no distinction between them except in the imperatives of the mission. Unless they are overcome by hatred.

I marvel at the human need to travel, at the determination to get from one place to another. We travel by boat, by bus, by tractor. If nothing exists any longer, we will walk, walk, walk, however many miles are required of us, through a trackless wilderness. We live most fully in those moments of danger in the crossing. Nothing deters us. One time, when the peace negotiations failed, Suresh was making the crossing. They were off-loaded from the tractor and asked to run for their lives as planes came swooping down like a covey of birds.

Now as the war continues and our attention turns to destruction, I wonder at the futility of what I am learning. All my intricate drawings, those notes in my file, the drawings in the lecture rooms on the whiteboards—of what use are they to us now? I have calculated precisely and drawn with the most meticulous care roads and bridges, made achitects' blueprints of soaring towers and deep tunnels. But bridges will be blown up, roads mined, the strongest concrete structures will cave in with flying glass splinters that blind eyes and decapitate bodies, which will lie buried in debris.

There used to be a church at Kilaly, where we embarked. They say that a miracle had taken place there during the Portugese occupation of the north in the sixteenth century. One of our generals, who was fighting on the side of the Portuguese forces, was on a march with his troops, to attack his own kind. He was weary, so the story goes, and took some time off to rest beneath a tree. He fell asleep and dreamt of an ambush. If he proceeded along a certain route, he and his men would be annihilated. In his dream, a saint—was it Sebastian?—appeared to him and indicated that buried deep within the soil at that very spot was a statue of a saint, which possessed miraculous powers, as well as sacred relics. When the general awoke, he related the dream to his men. They unearthed the statue and the relics. The general and his men took another route and ambushed the enemy, those of his own kind. To commemorate the escape from certain death, a church was eventually built at that very spot by the general's family. Until these troubled times came upon this land, centuries later, long after the Portuguese had been violently dislodged by the Dutch, and the Dutch by the British, the statue and the sacred relics were taken in procession at the annual church feasts. The statue remained in the church.

The family moved to the capital of the island long ago. I don't think they will ever return. The church must be in ruins, if any part of it still remains. The relics may still be in the possession of the general's descendents. And the statue? Ambushes are a common occurrence now.

When we were leaving Kilaly, I had looked around to see if I could see the ruins of the church, but there was nothing I could detect. The landscape was enshrouded in darkness.

There is talk, though, that the units of the army that have been posted to the north read sacred words from the Bible before they go on their forays, sacred words that will protect them. It is said that a particular battalion which does this has the least losses. Perhaps sacred words do work and protect the believer. 'Om,' I say to myself, 'Om.'

In olden days, churches had pews for the higher castes; those belonging to the lower castes sat on the floor. It is ironic that there were such inequalities in the house of god, but none in our journey through the night, in the boat or on the tractor.

The tractor arrives. We climb in, hold on precariously. The pressure of other human bodies is everywhere. With every lurch, jerk and jolt, the wedged-in bodies provide us with a sense of security, a shared humanity.

When we reach Omanthai, I prepare to walk to Vavuniya. There is no alternative to this. It is three kilometres to the main road, from where we can take a conveyance to continue the journey. The checkpoints still lie ahead.

II

I disembark from the boat that carried me from Kilaly to Alangerni. I take a few faltering steps, away from the rest of the travellers, and walked almost blindly along the sands, stumbling and dazed. My clothes cling to my body, wet with the waters of the lagoon, smelling of fish. I carry my sandals in my hands, soaked and sodden, the soles encrusted with sand. My pink satin underskirt is like fishskin against my limbs; slithery with smoothed-down scales. Is my body undergoing some form of metamorphosis? Fish struggling on the shore as the fishermen fling them from their wide nets. And turtles too, their flesh exposed to the knives of slaughter. Myths and legends surface in my mind. Fish and womb. The Great Mother. The yoni. Vessel of the fish. Friday. Fish-eating among the Catholics. The Greek word *ikhthus* representing Jesus Christ, son of God. The two crescent moons making up the fish symbol. Latin—*vesica piscis*. I wish I could slip back into the waters of the lagoon and submerge myself in the waves.

I must change into dry clothes . . . but where? I see a kovil in the distance, enclosed in silence and seemingly empty of humans. Perhaps there I can change before I join the others for the next stage of our journey.

As I walk towards the kovil, I wonder how long it has been a temporary refuge for transients like myself. This was the first time I was crossing by boat. Earlier, I would usually take a bus, one of the special air-conditioned buses with piped music to enliven the journey which regularly carried passengers out of the peninsula. The landmarks on that long drive had grown familiar to me, the stops and changes were predictable. We would take food wrapped in plantain leaves and carried in baskets woven from dried palmyrah fronds— red rice, stringhoppers, vegetables, fried fish, fish curry, a container of *sodhi* flavoured with dill seed. There would be Thermos flasks of hot coriander-flavoured coffee and bottles of drinking water from our wells. And there would be gifts for friends and relatives in the south: different kinds of mangoes, nectar-sweet and ripe, hand-plucked from laden branches; bundles of tender *murunga*; *odial kelengu*, the crisp and fibrous dried palmyrah root which we could break off into pieces and crunch.

Sometimes we would also travel south by train. I would sit by the window of the compartment and watch the white sandy dunes of Chavakachcheri give way to the red earth of Chunnakam. All along the way, there would be palmyrah groves, the tall, straight palms with their flourishing crests of fronds, laden with clusters of dark brown fruit like polished mahogany. The *kalpa* tree, the tree of life, transplanted from paradise by Brahma, which has eight hundred and one uses according to folk legend. I loved watching the familiar sights: laden mango trees, the farmers working on their land in the light of early morning, herds of goats wandering about searching for grass and leaves, fences made of the huge fan-like fronds of dried palmyrah, the murunga trees with branches like delicate green filigree. At the southern boundary of the peninsula, there was Elephant Pass where once the elephant herds from the mainland would cross the ford to eat the ripening palmyrah fruit that grew on the other side of the estuary. I remember the glistening white salterns and the Dutch fort in the distance, now converted into a resthouse, the waters of the ocean lapping the sides of the walls. But now we have to take alternate routes out of the peninsula . . .

And the new route has brought me to this kovil, I think as I place my sandals to the side of the entrance and push open the doors. Fortunately for me, they are not padlocked. But they are made of heavy carved wood and I have to use all my strength to open them. Inside, there is a cool, womb-like darkness. The fragrance of camphor and incense cling to the walls. The flagged stone floor is smooth beneath my bare blistered feet. I feel the great silence enwrap me.

There is a strange translucent light shining through the kovil. It gleams golden. Gold—such a feminine colour, and so befitting the statues of the goddesses I now see amidst the darkness. In the dim half-light, it seems as if there are invisible lamps of gold glowing. Perhaps it is the memory of flames that once burned brightly in tiered brass lamps. The glow illuminates the faces and limbs of the deities, so that they are no longer concealed in darkness. They appear almost to breathe as they gaze at me. Their expressions are calm and serene, devoid of the turmoil, the sadness and pain I had observed on the faces of my fellow travellers in the boat. The goddesses seem to be listening for the echoes of the chanting of Sanskrit slokas and singing of *thevarams*, the memory of which clings to these walls.

I feel an unknown emotion. I seem to have somehow just entered the true house of the gods. The worshippers must now be few and far between but the spirit of bhakti pervades the place. I can feel it, it is palpable like a breath of wind. It stirs something buried deep within my innermost being, still alive, yet breathing and waiting for me to summon it forth.

There is no one in this kovil to chant the Sanskrit slokas for the pujas, no worshippers to sing thevarams. I wish there had been something I could listen to, as I used to listen to the church litany, from which I drew so much comfort. I need comfort now. So I sing, very softly, beneath my breath, the hymns familiar to me. Though addressed to a different god, the words evoke the same spirit of devotion. I feel I am singing new songs to deities far more ancient, deities who were here long, long before Christian missionaries came to the north. I feel no sense of division. A place of worship, whether it be the kovil or the church, will always be sanctuary. The deities surround me, so some of my sense of loneliness begins to disperse.

What does the believer come here to seek? Moksha? A realization of the Absolute? Or to fulfill a vow? Or to do penance for wrongdoing? As a Christian, for me the path to salvation is one that is fraught with suffering; Christ is the Good Shepherd, I am the lost sheep. These are the images that I have grown up with . . . In the churches where I worship, I have gazed long upon the face of the crucified Christ who bears on his head a crown of thorns and whose hands and feet are nailed to the cross. My mind fills with pain, agony, sin, penance. Hope lies only in the thought of the Resurrection and in the knowledge that a living Christ walked with us in all our travails. The Christian missionaries imparted these messages to my people from churches which had been built by colonizers and conquerors. Their pulpits were the pulpits of a different kind of power: earthly conquest, temporal power. The conquerors had invaded this land but the effects of their invasions had lasted for a limited space. Now it is only in historical documents that one finds knowledge of their tenure. I wonder what kind of sermons they preached. All ghosts.

The kovil gleams golden. Gold will never perish, gold that is inseparably associated with womanhood, with brides. I still preserve the small amounts of gold I possess, the gold that adorned me when I was married. Some of it is sewn into little pockets on my bodice, to pay for the journey, for tickets. I am a Christian yet I too had a dower of gold, like all brides on our island through the ages as they sit on the *manaverai*. But that is all changing now. The young women who now fight for the Cause are warriors, for them there is a new kind of chastity. For them, the ageless gold has taken on new meaning. Now it is to buy guns with, or passages to the south.

But both loving bride and fierce warrior are aspects of the goddess. Siva Shakti, the great mother of the universe, the goddess in her many incarnations: Kali and Durga; creator, preserver and destroyer; yet instinct with maternal love, protecting her young. Maybe that is why I feel so much at harmony in this place. The goddess and I have this love in common. My journey is undertaken out of this love, to see my younger son in the south. Shakti, the mother of the universe, the mother of all creation. But there are two pujas for her: Durga puja and Kali puja. It is Kali who seems more powerful in today's world. There are terrifying images of her, stamping on all evil, brandishing the heads of the giants she had slain, and wearing a string of skulls round her neck.

I pause to think how strange it is that though I am a

Christian, I feel so completely at home here. Ancient racial memories arise within me as I look upon the face of Shakti. I wish I could make an offering to her. Many mothers do so for the safety and protection of their sons and daughters, some of whom they will never see again. The sons and daughters of today do not taste the nectar of the gods as we did during our youth. Their youth is overshadowed by the cyanide capsule they may finally have to bite.

My life is so limited. I am a mother. For me, it is enough to love and take care of my sons. No one will ever hear my name or of what I have done. But those young women whose bodies become live explosions, even if their names are not known for certain, their deeds become historical, recorded for all time. They are the modern-day incarnations of the Great Mother as Kali, the destroyer who devours all existence.

I am just one speck among the vast multitudes in this world. If my life is snuffed out, there will be only a few to mourn. People do not have time to share other people's grief nowadays. Everyone who has lived in the peninsula, has known grief and loss. In the south, too. There are mothers everywhere who have not even received the bodies of their children for burial. We see the rows of neatly laid-out, sprawling bodies with the grimace of death on their faces . . . And then we forget, except for those who have lost the one who has meant everything to them—father, brother, sister, son, daughter . . .

My consciousness becomes a crater which swallows up all thoughts of those deaths, burying them deep, deep within its very depths to surface only in nightmares. I shudder for an instant.

My two sons are not militants. They are ordinary young men, I do not know what they they believe in this struggle for a separate homeland. My elder son has managed to study in a prestigious college in the south, the younger to do an Honours course in engineering and to become an assistant lecturer in his university. What if he had been one of those who had to bite on a cyanide capsule at so young an age? Sacrifice. Isn't it part of all our religions?

What if I had a daughter? What if she had joined the movement? The young girls have broken away from all the constraints imposed on them by tradition. There are regiments of women, there are the suicide bombers, there are the Sea Tigers. Today's women fulfil different roles. Yet they have suckled from the breasts of their mothers who no doubt hoped that they too would grow up to bear their own children . . . We have to try to understand them, their missions, their sacrifice of life and youth . . . We have to try to understand why such choices are made. We have to question ourselves, why someone else's child and not mine?

I think of the great temple festival at Nallur, when the deities are all decked out in silks, satins, velvets and brocades embellished with silver and gold, gem-encrusted *padakkams*, heavy gold chains, sovereigns dangling from every inch of their bodies, garland upon garland of fragrant flowers round their necks. Towards the end of the festival, they are taken out in the chariot, along the temple *veedhi*. The penitent would perform his penance, rolling and rolling his body along the veedhi, clothed only in his *veshti*. By the end, his limbs would be coated with the white dust stirred up by that movement. Will that veedhi one day be empty of all worshippers? Who will blow the conch to echo over the deserted plains? And the ancient rites and rituals? Who will perform them? The gods will remain within their sanctum and perhaps the echoes of the slokas will linger. But who will carry the puja trays to them in a ghost town where shells rain down like bursts of lethal fireworks, where the bombs fall, and when the exodus begins, as some day it will. Perhaps an ancient *pusari* will remain to help the new conquerors to carry out the rites and rituals which they too believe in; sacred rites still must have significance to these warriors.

And we? We cannot think of time in such cosmic sweeps. We can only live from day to day. We predict time through light, through dark. Dawn. Midday. Dusk. Nightfall. And the passing of the seasons. The seasons of drought and rain. We keep moving. Everybody is constantly moving, within the peninsula and out of it. But the deities remain. They will always remain. Their ears are now accustomed to more than the chanting of the slokas. The bursting of the shells reverberate like the sound of conches in the past which announced the commencement of each new battle . . . But the deities are still the guardians of this land. They do not make the same crossings as we do, their garments drenched in the waters of the lagoon, but the worshippers still carry them in their hearts. Bombs fall on churches and kovils, and their walls are shattered by shells. But those whom we worship remain in spirit. Perhaps their presence even in the ruins are a solace and a refuge to those who are left behind. For me, now, this kovil is more than a place of refuge. The face of Shakti engenders in me a feeling of power.

Now that we have to move away from the well-tried paths and the conventional routes, we have no other alternative but to find the strength and power to carry on. Though war transforms the safe road, we still have to travel along it. There are no alternatives to reach a desired destination.

Time is now fraught with all kinds of dangers, visible and invisible. My mind turns to those biblical times when the waters of the Red Sea parted for the Israelites to cross to the other side . . . 'Then Moses stretched out his hand over the sea; and the Lord caused the sea to go back by a strong east wind all that night, and made the sea into dry land, and the waters were divided. So the children of Israel went into the midst of the sea on the dry ground and the waters were a wall to them on their right hand and on their left . . .'

There has not been such an exodus for us, not yet. But perhaps very soon, that too will take place. Perhaps the crossing is an intimation of what will come to pass. The waters did not part for the passage of our boat but I reached dry land somehow. I leave behind a son, a daughter-in-law and a grandchild, and my home. I hope to return one day but who knows whether I will. I only hope to survive for as long as the time allotted to me. We who make our journeys must brave fire and ice, ocean and desert, whether it be here, in our own terrain or elsewhere in a far country where the millions of asylum seekers and refugees from their own war-torn zones trek into an unknown future. Many will never reach Canaan, the promised land, but perish on the way. There is now no one place which can be called home. Within this one country, two exist, one of them engendered by new imperatives, historical imperatives. The conflict grows daily into monstrous proportions. Death and displacement are the inevitable results. Will the chasm be closed in one day by the piled up bodies of the dead?

Life in the past centred around journeys were easy to take—family reunions, marriages, births, death. We travelled south from the peninsula without thinking this was a journey of any significance. No one looked upon us as if we were a different breed of people. Now we have to re-examine our identities and ask ourselves about those first incursions and invasions and how we even arrived here. I think of the history books from which I once studied and in turn taught . . . Are we descended from those first colonizers from the subcontinent? Were these colonizers responsible for the collapse of ancient civilizations which had existed on the island. Did the invader ever become one with the invaded? Or will ancient grudges always remain? It is not easy for anyone to accept submission, to be under the yoke. *Sub iugum*, as the missionaries taught us in my Latin class. Nowhere in the world will the young accept it. But along with the ideal of freedom, have they also been taught that all people other than themselves are to be seen as 'the enemy'? Now we travel from the north to the south to see our children as they set out on their own journeys as asylum seekers. But not our people alone. Others too have to undertake new journeys. Their motives may be different but we all seek, in spite of all obstructions, the route to where we want to go. The ordinary journey now ceases to be a commonplace, everyday fact of life, but becomes a mission.

Standing here in this kovil, I think of the battles I have read about in books. And I think about those who are seldom mentioned in these battles but are nevertheless an integral part of them. Women. They were a part of the armies of the ancient times, especially the barbarian armies. In the Bible, in the Book of Judges, Barak, who commanded an army of ten thousand men, refused to go to battle unless the prophetess Deborah, wife of Lapidoth, accompanied him. And the Roman historian, Tacitus—yes, I remember my history lessons—spoke of the Druid forces who repelled the invaders on the island of Mona. Among the soldiers, he wrote, there were black-clad women who waved swords and cursed the enemy like the Furies. They were supposed to have magic battle cries that made the enemy weak. And there were Islands of Women where the Amazons lived without men. It was only when they wanted to conceive children that they had anything to do with a man. Women there were, who as late as the eighteenth century, wore men's clothes, rode astride on horseback, and fought beside men in war. And now our daughters fight too, putting aside the traditions of our society, dressing in battle fatigues, and carelessly shearing off their wealth of hair.

And if I was young? What if it were years and years ago, before I was married and had children? I wonder what I would have made of my life in these times if I were a young woman.

Within this space of time in which my thoughts wander endlessly, exploring different routes, alternate paths of the mind, my life has undergone a sea change. For perhaps the first time since this war began, a sense of peace steals over me as I stand here, feeling the ancient rites which permeate every part of this abode enter me, within my whole mind, spirit and body, reaching the core of my inner being. But thinking of myself reminds me of my two sons. I must go to one of them. It is time for me to move on.

I have forgotten that I entered into this kovil with a sense of self-pity for lost times, chilled to the bone as if rigor mortis was setting in. But now I remember that I have to change my wet clothes before I emerge to continue along the land route. Wouldn't it be an act of sacrilege to change before the gaze of the deities? What shall I do? Find the darkest shadowy corner, conceal myself behind a pillar and unwrap the folds of my sari in such a way that nothing of my flesh is seen? As I think of each meticulously arranged and folded pleat of my sari, I realize how constricting they have been all my life. Especially when I had to step off the sandy verge of the lagoon earlier and wade through shoulder-high water for about a hundred yards, and when I reached the rocking boat and clambered in.

I conceal myself in the darkest niche, hidden in the shadows. I begin to shed the garments that clothed me but as I do so, a strange force seems to take over my body. I feel my flesh being transmuted into another substance—one other than this mortal flesh, the substance of which Shakti's image is composed. I seem to share her breath. I felt that this sanctuary had taken me in, accepted me, transformed me so that I could be at home here for time without end. I had lost my mortal hunger and thirst. I no longer needed fruit or nectar to keep me alive, I felt satiated from the fragrance of those past rituals which still lingered. It did not matter to me that there was no one to carry the puja trays. They would return, the worshippers. The rites had been repeated here so many times over, making this so sacred a place that my flesh-and-blood body had miraculously altered. I had come inside, quite lightheaded with exhaustion and hunger, in need of comfort. Now everything had changed. I seemed to have become one of the deities.

I could hear a voice very near me, softly speaking in syllables that I only faintly understood. This is not the language of ordinary parley which one uses in everyday raucous interchanges, but language such as the priest uses when worshipping. Miraculously, I could understand it. It flowed through my mind and imagination to become that which could be comprehended, for now I shared the same breath as the goddesses, although I was newly-born and they were ancient. But I felt I was no intruder here. I was welcome.

'Make yourself at home within this sanctuary. We understand you are here after a long journey. You have travelled through time, through memory, to reach us. We can create a space for you here too.'

The tremors that had shaken my limbs seem to have passed. I touch my body. It is as if invisible hands have very gently unwrapped my wet clothes and covered me with fresh, dry clothes out of the bundles I carried. The wet clothes, still dripping with water, lie at my feet. I look up at the faces of the goddesses. Which one of them had been

107

speaking to me? Do they speak in separate voices? They belong to time without age. What patience they have cultivated, day after day, month after month, year after year; changeless, while the penitents themselves grow old and died, while the priests and pusaries changed. The slokas never changed, only the human voices that chanted them.

'Take up your abode here,' the voice continued. 'No shells fall here. You will be safe. There are no mines laid where you stand. Take a few steps, walk towards that niche that stands empty and remain there for all time.'

The idea was tempting. To remain here, among the divine, with my spirit forever filled with the sense of peace and tranquility I have now. I have known so much suffering, widowed young, bringing up two sons alone, shells falling on the house. I know that the deities too are accustomed to the sounds of battle. Yet, they endure. Always. They will always endure. And I can endure with them.

But time passes. I have to make my decision. When I made my decision to travel south, I had to prepare myself to face the hazards of the journey. I first had to prepare my mind and then my body. Age did not matter. The ancient ones climb Adam's Peak in their pilgrimage for that is the sacred mountain where the Buddha has placed the impression of his foot. It is the inner strength of faith and belief that sustains each one of them. It was that inner faith which had given me the courage to face the passage through water, arid plain and jungle. And my son at the end of the journey. Will he miss me if he never sees me again? If I stay on in this abode of peace?

'Stay!' the voice says. 'Stay with us.'

I stoop to pick up my clothes. My limbs feel warm. I feel a different kind of life flowing through my body. I am human again, but I have a strange new strength to carry me through the next stage, and the next, and the next, of my journey as I walk out into the starkness of white sunlight and white sand.

The Wall

EARLY ONE MORNING, the sound of loaded lorries lumbering up the road to the house next door woke all of us. Over the next few days, the rocks and stones, bricks and sand deposited by the lorries began to pile up at the foot of the drive.

We were excited at the prospect of having new neighbours. We were townspeople, but we had moved to this little housing colony in the village some years ago. We loved the rare peace of our life here. All around were hills and fields. Even are our garden seemed part of the wilderness, full of grasshoppers, centipedes, wild hare and birds. Often rare migratory birds perched on the jam fruit tree.

'Aren't you going to do something about the garden?' a friend had asked Louise, looking out at the overgrown ground around our house. 'No,' she had answered, 'I like the garden undisturbed. It's the way it was before we came here. It's we who are intruders displacing the birds and animals. I want to live at peace with them, as do people here. We left the city because people there perpetually encroached onto your preserves. So here I let the grass grow tall so that the wild hare will always have safety and cover.'

When the rains came, the seared and parched grass became green. There were now wild marigolds scattered all over like a dusting of golden pollen. Unknown plants sprang up, rank yet rich with life. The king crows spread out their stately tail feathers and flashed their ruby-red eyes as they walked grandiosely through the courtyard of grass. The mynahs and *selalihis* walked about sedately, the sun filtering through their glossy wings. The seven sisters, sleek and grey, grew fat with feeding on insects and grubs. The kingfisher perched patiently on the edge of the water tank, waiting to scoop up tadpoles and fish. If you turned up the soil, it squirmed with worms, brown and pink, and fat white grubs. The wild hare nibbled the new grass. There was no partition between the village and garden, only a broken wooden fence through which the hare could creep.

We heard that the house next door had been bought for a family from the neighbouring village of Aruppola by a German doctor. There was a story behind this. One of the sons, Ajith, had been a roomboy in a five-star hotel in Kandy when he had met this doctor, who was travelling through the country, and he had invited him back to Germany. Other members of the family had followed, and they were reputed to be wealthy after many years of living there. Ajith had bought a minibus and set up a bus service for the village. Their German patron, Herr Doktor as they called him, also had provided the money for extensive renovations to the house. The understanding was that Herr Doktor and his friends would spend their winters here, and they would be

114

looked after by Ajith's family.

When Ajith and his family first moved in and renovations began, Louise tried to be friendly in the way usual in our community. She met Ajith one day as they were both walking up the hill. She introduced herself and asked politely how he liked living in this village.

'Would you like to come and see the dancing in the village this evening?' she asked by way of conversation. 'Some of the best dancers from the village will be performing. Ukkuwa will be dancing his famous *vannams*, with Suramba on the drums.'

The traditional dancers lived close to the housing scheme in the village where they enjoyed the gifts of land given them in the days of the Kandyan kings for performing their feudal services and dancing in the court at ceremonial occasions. Some of the older dancers had been taken many years ago to Germany by Hagenbeck for his famous circus. They had returned to live peaceful lives among their paddy fields. During the *perahera* season, clad in their Ves regalia, they leaped and cavorted to the thudding drums in the centre of a circle of torch-bearers while the flames blazed away like kites on fire, scattering shimmering sparks in the darkness.

'No, no, ah, you see . . . I have seen many dances in Germany . . .'

'Ah, you have seen the best European ballet?'

'Oh, I have much business, much work. Time, I don't have.'

'Yes, with your minibus, you must have lots of work. You're very busy, aren't you?'

115

'Yes, yes!'

Ajith and his brothers had many expensive things in the house: cameras, cassette players and other electronic goods which they had brought back from their sojourn abroad. This conspicuous wealth isolated them from the other residents of the housing colony, as did their close relationship with their foreign patron and the fact that they had lived abroad for many years. They seemed to be living in two different worlds, have two different sets of loyalties: the ties that bound them to their birthplace in the neighbouring village, and their closeness to the Germans. Perhaps because of this, they felt it wiser to keep their lives private, and made no attempt to become part of the close community of the housing estate and of the village. They made it clear that they wanted no intrusion into their affairs.

That winter, Herr Doktor and his friends came to visit for the first time. The tall banks that separated our two houses hid from us a world that the whole housing colony and village were intensely curious about. On the bank behind the other house, the Germans sunbathed. There was a specially built cement water tank where Ajith and his brothers bathed, pouring bucket after bucket of sun-warmed water on their bodies. The Germans however always bathed indoors in the imported porcelain bathtubs that had recently been installed. There were also new toilets and a garage.

The rumour in the village said that plans were being drawn up for a summer house and a swimming pool. There was endless conjecture among the villagers about which new structure would come up next as they passed up and down the pathway that ran through the extensive grounds of the house on their way to the river. 'There's going to be a walled-in section with steps leading upwards for the *sudu mahatthaya* to sit and enjoy the view,' one of them informed Julius. From the terrace, Herr Doktor could see the tranquil landscape: the blue-green ranges and the fertile fields; white cranes flying over the meandering river, fleeting arrows against a darkening evening sky; sunsets that flamed against the horizon. White *dagobas* and temples dotted the distant green hills. Kites soared in the windy season, sailing among the puff-ball clouds.

We heard more about the doctor through the village grapevine. During World War II, he had been captured by the Russians and taken to Siberia, where he had had to work with pick and shovel. This had ruined his health forever, which was why he wanted to spend his winters in the island.

We saw the Germans frequently but had never talked to them. One evening, however, Julius was invited next door. On his return he described the experience to us. The house was spotless, he said, the polished floors shone like mirrors. He was led from room to room. There were built-in seats at the windows. The shower came from Morocco, the carpet from Italy, the glass and ceramic from Sweden. The delicious smell of soup cooking filled the kitchen. No smoke-blackened walls marred the spotless interior. The stainless steel utensils of food gleamed on the German electric hot plates. Herr Doktor even took Julius to the toilet. Disinfectant, polish, clean antiseptic smells, rolls of imported toilet paper; a chamber which kept out all human odours. Yes, the whole house smelt of disinfectant and polish, Julius said.

'I wish I could live in a clean, well-ordered house,' said Mira.

'Yes,' Louise said, 'like whose? But you won't have the same parents, remember. No reading and eating in bed, no leaving unwashed cups and tumblers on window ledges, books beneath unmade beds.'

'Yes,' Mira persisted, 'yes, but I would be different if the house were in order.'

Louise gazed at our faces as we sat round her. Her mouth began to droop at the corners. She looked round our house, at all the familiar objects, the dust on the centre table, the ring marks left on it by coffee and tea cups, the floor where the dog had scratched itself and shed some fur. And in the garden facing the front door, the jam fruit tree had fallen, uprooted in the winds. The wood was rotting, eaten by termites.

'You should see the lighting in the drawing room, the bedrooms, the kitchen,' said Julius, 'soft, subdued . . .'

For a while, Julius felt dissatisfied. Herr Doktor's lifestyle made our home seem disordered and plain. But unlike us, Herr Doktor did not have a large, laughing family living together. We knew, from popular lore in the village, he had no family. There was an unmarried sister who lived her own life in Germany. Which was perhaps why he had settled in our small village. With his money, he was now able to purchase companionship and play patron to Ajith and his brothers.

But we wondered how long this would last, the intimacy of their companionship. Despite the young men's adoption of German lifestyle, their links with their family continued. Their father still brought them food cooked by their mother in the village home in stainless steel food carriers. One day,

118

the young men would surely want to break away and find wives for themselves. Then they would have their own families and their need for Herr Doktor would cease. For the moment, they pandered to him. He had bought them the house, made it comfortable for himself and for them as well. They, too, enjoyed the power of money and of possessions. They cooked for the German and his friends. They drove them around in Herr Doktor's cars. Ajith's sister wore a little apron around her waist, like a maid in a fashionable European household, when she waited on the Germans. Herr Doktor glowed in the attention he got from this family who waited hand and foot on himself and his friends.

The day would surely come when the German would return and find his attendants were neglecting him, thought Louise. He would be compelled to say, 'This is the house I bought for you. If you do not look after me, then I will not leave you my money after I die.' And Ajith would say, 'Doesn't matter, old man. I don't want your money. I now have a wife and child. They mean more to me than your money.' The old man would have to beg them to care for him, and it would be pitiful to seen him return again and again because he had no one else to look after him.

One day Herr Doktor turned his attention to the garden. He set to work with a vengeance to set it in order. Ajith and his brothers had not bothered about it, and it looked as much of a wilderness as ours. One evening, a few weeks after he set to work, we were sitting in the veranda looking at the neighbouring house. In the growing darkness of the evening, it looked like a doll's house. It was as if a child had been at play, building at will. There was nothing natural or wild, a stark contrast to the fields and woods around. There were new parapet walls along the driveway, and cemented walk-ups. Nature was not allowed to have its will there. The tropical vegetation had been pruned and nurtured until it appeared European in its restraint. There were flowerbeds in geometric shapes and hedges meticulously trimmed. Against the hedge, the parapet stretched like the banisters of a stairway, hard-edged, smoothly cemented, grey. Flower pots, all of the same shape, size and colour, were placed at precise intervals along it. At the two ends stood enormous urns containing large plants. They were so large that they did not seem to belong to the garden. They belonged more to a dream of castles and palaces, with trout streams and lawns on which peacocks proudly strutted.

The old man's dream was an European dream, a dream he had had when he was a prisoner-of-war digging for potatoes in the frozen ground, waking up on a cold winter morning to find his comrade cold and dead by his side, thought Louise. Hence his desire for warmth, order and opulence. Yet he cannot escape from his prison. The sombre cement walls shut him and his friends in. He has withdrawn into the enclaves of his territory, imposing a pattern of life that was alien to that of the rest of the community. His house and garden were both palace and prison.

And as she sat there, thinking of him, through the closed windows of the neighbouring house, came the triumphant strains of Beethoven's 'Emperor Concerto'. The music was played softly. Herr Doktor did not want to disturb his neighbours.

We had thought that perhaps the distance between the

two houses would be bridged over time. But gradually it became quite apparent to us that the barriers would always be there. The silence between the two houses was complete. Though their voices reached our garden, the language was alien to our ears.

The Germans came and went with their pale, winter-bound faces. Their eyes were guarded. They were careful not to cast a single intrusive look at their neighbours, as much as to say, 'We will not invade your privacy, do not invade ours.' Their faces were serious in expression. They spoke only in German among themselves. They would lie in the sun for hours, allowing the sun to warm their bodies, to soak through the almost transparent covering of skin. A young German climbed a thambili tree. He was barebodied, his skin white as the moon. It was a wondrous new experience for him. He peered from the branches and the clusters of orange-red thambilis like a white stork that had flown in from over the river. Most of the Germans, however were middle-aged, round-cheeked, and well-dressed. They walked about the house as if there was a tropical jungle outside, explored the fields and woods in their high-heeled shoes and starched shirts. They smelt of expensive perfumes and colognes. Their cameras went click-click, snipping off little bits of the landscape, imprisoning a little bit of the sunlight to take back to the cold winter snows. Click-click-click, the sound was that of some migrant bird.

Our house stood on a higher elevation than Herr Doktor's. He must have wanted to extend his boundaries and wall in his newly acquired territory. It gradually became more and more important to him that there should be a wall, a high

121

wall, between the two houses, or so we later concluded when one morning we discovered that a wall was being built. Not merely between the two houses, but all around his property. As with the rapid action which ensued when he decided to put the garden in order, he took swift measures. Workers started coming along the dusty road by the river every morning. Perpetually smoking beedis and cigarettes, and wearing their bright batik sarongs, they soon became a familiar part of the landscape. The work looked streamlined and efficient, personally supervised by Herr Doktor. The men scurried about, scooping, shovelling, lifting, carrying, placing brick upon brick like ants. They first laid the first row of bricks all around the garden, snaking across the green hillside, cutting across the old paths down to the river that the villagers had always taken. Herr Doktor was now cut off from all the houses in the colony. Throughout the day the men worked, their heads padded with thick cloth turbans to bear the weight of the heavy pans of sand and bricks which they carried on their heads. They mixed the cement and concrete. The *baasuneha* laid on the cement smoothly and evenly with a trowel. The sound of metal grating against sand became a part of our consciousness. The young boys with their bare feet and bronzed bodies, black tousled hair shimmering with coconut oil, ran up and down the hill with wheelbarrows, scrunching on the tight-packed pebbles as they carted the bricks up from the bottom of the drive. Herr Doktor sat in the sun, overseeing his little kingdom and plotting the moves of the pawns on his chessboard garden.

'Ajith,' he called out periodically, 'tell them . . .' and he would give precise orders.

122

Michael and Otto, old friends from Denmark, came to visit us while this was going on. We sat in the garden and watched the wall grow.

'Why does the old man want all these walls?' Julius asked them. 'Do they build a lot of walls in Europe?'

They laughed. 'Oh yes, they love walls. In Germany, they build walls everywhere, on the beaches too,' Michael said.

'The English too. An Englishman's home is his castle, so he has to fortify it,' said Otto.

'Nazis,' commented Michael.

But we can live without walls, Louise thought. In this community, they are not necessary. For years we have lived at peace with our neighbours. This is not the city that we have to keep out trespassers and intruders. The villagers have their own lands that their families have ploughed and harvested for generations, from the times of the ancient Sinhala kings. They have no need of walls. We, the outsiders, the town dwellers, are all intruders here and now we come and change their lifestyles. We restrict their paths to the river when they go to bathe and fish, we even displace the animals which have to retreat further and further into the interior. Ancient demographic maps are being changed. Private kingdoms, walled into fortresses, and then what—warfare?

One day we saw an elegant white-painted gate swinging open and shut at the bottom of the drive. The wall was still only a few bricks high, but the gateposts had been built. Herr Doktor was very proud of it. He was standing by it as Julius came up the road, and for the first time in weeks, spoke to him.

'How long do you think it will last?' he asked Julius, stroking its sleek surface with almost sensual pleasure.

Julius noticed that the gate has taken a little bit extra of the road, a foot or two more of land that was not part of the doctor's property.

'Will it last? How long?' Herr Doktor persisted.

Julius laughed, not quite sure what to say in the face of this insistence on longevity. 'Well, if you and I last as long as this gate, we'll be lucky. What do you say, Herr Doktor?

The old German was silent. It was not a laughing matter to him. He was already an old man.

'Maybe he feels threatened in a foreign land,' Louise said when Julius narrated this incident to her. 'The wall will keep away all intruders. He and his friends will be protected from all whom they wish to exclude from their precious territory.'

Meanwhile, the construction continued. As the wall grew, we realized what it would mean for us, for our way of life. It would block out the pure shining curve of the river as it flowed sinuous and serpentine, disappearing into the range of hills nearby. We would no longer be able to see the solitary boats drifting over the water. No, we did not want this wall.

'Stop building that wall,' Julius finally said to the baas.

The baas was displeased. Ajith, summoned to the scene, was impatient. Of course the wall would be built. How could anyone challenge the all-powerful Herr Doktor? Such undermining of power and authority disturbed them.

'Herr Doktor is going back to Germany in two weeks. The wall must be built before he goes.' Ajith was firm.

'Your wall is encroaching on my land. I must look after

the interests of my landlord. You must get the land surveyed to ascertain where my land ends and yours begins,' Julius said patiently.

'Don't worry. I will give you some of this land. You take two feet. Good, then? I give you two feet.' Ajith's tone was persuasive.

'No, you can't just play around with land like that. There are rules and surveys. Besides, we don't want the wall. It will shut out the view.'

'Herr Doktor wants the wall. He goes back to Germany in two weeks. The wall must be completed before he goes,' Ajith insisted.

'Look,' said Julius with a firmness most uncharacteristic of him, 'if you continue building the wall where it is now, you are encroaching on my property. I need to inform my landlord, who is a government official in Colombo. We can do nothing without his permission.'

Ajith retreated without a word. But the building operations ceased. As the days passed, the bricks, piled up in neat blocks, grew weathered. The workmen sat around, smoking and chatting. The baas was fretting. He expected to make a lot of money from this wall, and now the work was on hold.

'What about the wall?' Ajith asked every other day.

'Have you worked out where the boundaries are?' countered Julius.

Ajith was silent. That land would have to be first surveyed. The hillside was becoming a battlefield. The date for Herr Doktor's departure came and went. The wall remained half-built.

But the wall was there, not visible but growing stronger daily, thought Louise. Invisible but impenetrable. We can all feel it. The silence grows between our two homes. It's like a war, thought Louise. Herr Doktor looks over territory, prepares for fresh conquests. Soon there will be guards, and watchdogs, prisoners who are desperate for escape. Each army stands on either side of a no man's land. The world shrinks in.

The parapet by the drive and the urns looked melancholy and funereal. Even the birds stayed away, and as the months passed, we all became aware of ownership, proprietary rights and territory. The sharp-bladed *hana* plants out thrust their sword-like leaves and grew rampant on the bank. Herr Doktor's garden began to look diminished with so much cutting and pruning. He had envisaged a Rhine dream in snowbound Siberia. Only, in reality it had turned out to be a fortified prison.

One day Ajith climbed up the bank. 'Herr Doktor has decided not to build a wall,' he announced, the emissary bringing news of the peace treaty. 'Herr Doktor says that you and I are good neighbours. We do not need walls.'

Herr Doktor went back to Germany shortly after this. We did not see him before he left. He took Ajith's brother Lalith with him.

After he left, Ajith changed dramatically. Perhaps he was used to seeing the Germans in their own territory, he had not realized how prohibitive they would be in his own land. He came over one evening, after the New Year celebrations. He

126

had climbed over the half-built wall and called out exuberantly, 'Aunty, aunty.' He held out a brown paper bag.

'Look what Ajith has brought for us,' Louise said to us.

The *kewuns* had been made by his mother in their village home with its wood fire hearth. They were were dark with honey, glistening with oil, crunchy at the frilled edges, soft as a honey-sweet fruit within. He had brought *athirasa* too. Julius had invited him in and he spent the whole evening with us, talking endlessly.

'Germany is cold, very cold,' he said, 'the streets are covered with snow. It piles up so quickly. If it is not cleared away at once, it will cover the houses. Everything is white, white houses, white streets.' He shivered as he spoke. Some of the cold and frost still seemed to cling to him.

One evening soon after that, there was loud music from the house next door. Ajith had invited friends from his village. They drank and sang late into the night. They played music which surged into the darkness, some popular Sinhala film songs. It was as if he had to fill his ears with the music he have been forced to forget during those long German winters. They let the voice of the singer, plangent and plaintive, swoon through the night air. Before the song came to an end, they lifted the arm of the record player, and it began all over again. It was as if they did not want to lose the music ever again. The voice, rich and pulsating, sang those tender songs of nelum flowers and moonlight and love. They joined in the song. They laugh louder. Their voices rose, fumbling, then grasping that lost tune. They disturbed the neighbours but no one minded for they were making up for lost time.

Soon the German will return and Beethoven, Liszt and Wagner will be heard again. But softly, for Herr Doktor is very considerate. Even the triumphant strains of the Emperor Concerto will be muted. He is careful not to disturb his neighbours.

Samsara

A LITTLE WAY from our housing estate in Watapuluwa, there was a hollow where plants grew fecund and untrammeled, feeding on the moisture drawn from hidden springs. A few jackals lived there. At night, one could hear them.

'Once there were many jackals here,' Mudiyanse told me. 'Then it was wild and overgrown in the hollow and all around here. After the housing estate was built here, the jackals had no place to stay and swam across the river into the jungle. You can still hear the jackals at night. A strange sharp kind of barking sound. But once the jungle is cleared, I don't know where they will move. The monitor lizards and iguanas too are almost disappearing.'

Once there had been jungle all around. Many years ago, British planters had cleared the jungle for their cocoa plantation. 'The planters lived here like kings in those days,' Mudiyanse said. Life had been very different before that in this village. It had hardly been a village, merely the scattered dwellings of a few families who belonged to the Govi caste and shared kinship ties; surrounded by their paddy fields and groves of breadfruit, jak trees, kitul and arecanut palms. The people who lived within these hidden groves had been here centuries before the British had conquered the Kandyan kingdom.

When we first came to live in the housing estate in Watapuluwa, filled with the American-style houses which were fashionable at that time, I would occasionally see this innocuous-looking individual wandering around with his dogs. I probably would not have really noticed him, except that I observed that he walked carefully avoiding looking at other people and never talked to anyone. There was a silent alertness about him, which reminded me of wild hares which move through the grass, always alert that predators may be around. Or like the wild mongoose which would dart suddenly across the road and vanish into the clumps of sunflower bushes and *ala kola* which flared open like cobra hoods. I felt an instinctive stirring of pity for this unknown man who seemed somehow alien and apart.

I learnt his name some time later. We needed someone to clear the wilderness in our garden, and one of the neighbours sent Mudiyanse along. He didn't speak very much that first day. A few days later, I had left the book I was reading on a chair in the veranda when I had gone inside the house for something. When I came out, Mudiyanse was looking closely at it.

'Can you read? Do you want to read this book?' I asked him.

He told me that he had studied in the Baptist Mission School in Watapuluwa when he was young. I wondered why

132

he was doing the kind of work he was doing if he had had that kind of education, though the lessons taught in the missionary school in those colonial times had little or no relevance to his life and survival in the village. But most of his former classmates must be leading far more prosperous lives. It was then that I heard about the central tragedy of Mudiyanse's life.

His father had sent him to school, he said. His mother had died when he was an infant and his father had carried him in his arms all the way from Pillawela to Watapuluwa after his mother's death. Before he could walk, his father would carry him around in his cloth. His father had loved him greatly. He had sent him to school hoping that one day he would be looked up to in his community for his learning. But his father had died when he was still young. His brothers had removed him from school.

Mudiyanse could not believe that his father would not have left him any part of his land. The fields too had been his rightful inheritance and yet the land had passed to his brothers who had sold some of the acres so that they passed from hand to hand.

His memories of being carried all the way to Watapuluwa where his father had looked after him in the house built by the thambili tree were very powerful. Would such a father have denied his son one out of the many acres he possessed? His brothers and sisters had their shares of land apportioned out, their fields, buffaloes and cattle. In his mind the fields belonged rightfully to him. He had a right to his share. He had inherited it from his father. But it had all been taken away from him. The obsession corroded his mind.

133

After his father's death, he had tried to resume his education. 'I was sent to Kapugoda priest's temple by my uncle,' he told us. 'When I arrived I was well looked after. There was plenty of paddy in the *attuwa*. I ate rice fresh from the harvest with a curry of coconut milk and maldive fish. They wanted me to be a monk. The next day, Kapugoda *hamuduru* called me and said, "Mudiyanse, all that land is overgrown with thorny bushes, the grass grows wild, clear it."

'I wanted to read, I wanted to study the *Tripitaka* about the teachings of the Buddha, not clear land and sweep the compound and fetch water from the well . . . So the next day I left the temple and returned home.'

My daughter was listening to our conversation. 'They must have sent him to the temple because his horoscope was not favourable,' she told me later.

One day I asked my next-door neighbour why Mudiyanse was thought to be mad by his own people. He worked in all our gardens untiringly. His only idiocyncratic habit to me was that he carried on monologues with himself, perhaps to mitigate his own sense of loneliness.

'Mudiyanse talks endlessly about his *paminilla* to reclaim his lost inheritance. His people deny that he has any rights to the land,' my neighbour explained. That denial in the face of his helplessness must have been corrosive. Together with that early betrayal by his own kith and kin.

He always seemed to be alone, with no friends or family. Where were all those children whom he had studied with in school? Grown up, still part of the village? Or had they moved away? Many of them perhaps still lived here but had

134

silently rejected him because he was different from them. Even his own family was blind to his innate wisdom and knowledge. They made him an outsider.

It was over books that we became friends. I gave him books from my library which he pored over. He especially liked ones on science and travel. We gradually discovered that he often went hungry and so we would invariably offer him food. He would sit on the corner of the veranda at the old table at which I had studied as a little girl with his plate of food and his pile of books beside him. Occasionally, I would place new books in the little pile of books on the table. Often he would spend all evening reading. When he felt sleepy, he would wish us goodnight and make his lonely way back to the village.

Mudiyanse lived behind our housing estate, where the houses stuck like awkward protuberances in the landscape, unlike the houses in the original village, which merged in with the earth. Reminiscent of boils and warts waiting to burst into suppurating sores, I had thought when I first saw them. But we had little choice. We were both teachers, we had a family, and money was scarce. Man-made barriers fenced off the housing estate from the wilderness where the true life of the village lay.

Mudiyanse had helped in the construction of many of the houses on the housing estate. He had cut the sod and levelled the earth for people to build their houses of brick, stone and concrete. He had chopped wood; he had trimmed and trammelled the wild strangling undergrowth that insidiously tried to creep back and throttle the new abodes. He also acted as caretaker for the houses that were still being constructed, guarding other peoples' belongings and territory. In his innocence, he did not question his displacement as a result of the new inroads made into the life of the village.

While he guarded other people's property, he had almost none of his own. All he had was his *wadiya*, a little piece of land where he had his hut, a makeshift structure to sleep in. It was more of a lair than a home, a fragile shelter covered on all sides with dried coconut fronds to keep out the rain or the cold night air. It was by a thambili tree, under which, he told me, his father was buried. There were a few fruit trees around it which he lovingly tended. His family had once owned all the land around his wadiya. His brothers still owned some of it. But they had little to do with him. Living among these fields, he was constantly reminded of his deprivation. His eternal grievance was for a share of paddy from the fields to which he insisted he had a claim. Every year, when Aluth Avurudha, the New Year, dawned and when his nieces brought us gifts of new rice from the fields, he would say, 'If only I had my paddy, I would have brought you a share too.'

When Mudiyanse was not reading, he wanted to talk about his paddy fields. He was obsessed with the rights denied him. Others collected the bushels of paddy from the harvest which rightfully belonged to him. This is what he talked about constantly in all the houses where he went to work. But nobody paid attention to his words. I asked my friends in the village about it. They said that Mudiyanse was the son of the second bed. The children of the first wife had greater claims, and they were not willing to let him have anything. His brothers had inherited a lot of land, but they

136

had sold off most of it.

I got to know one of his brothers, Malhamy. He was a quiet unobtrusive man with a hard-working wife and children. They had cows and buffaloes, and supplied the people of the housing estate with milk. They also had the paddy fields to till. His daughters would cut grass to feed the cattle, and sell some of it. Mudiyanse, on the other hand, often had to depend on the kindness of strangers for food. He could have moved away from the village to a nearby town where he would have earned more money. Yet he clung tenaciously to his hut and the trees around it. He was like one of the wild animals which still remain in their old lair in spite of the encroachment of humans who take over their habitats.

I noticed that Mudiyanse's voice was pitched at a slightly higher key than was normal. It climbed a different scale following its own musical notation with the slightest edge of hesitancy, travelling into the realm of bird cries and animal calls. He talked to the wind as he cut grass, planted seeds or plucked fruit in the garden. He lived in a world that embodied its unique form only for him, and was peopled by beings with whom only he could converse. They were not the ordinary beings who went about their own prosaic and mundane lives, like the villagers who ignored and abused him. It was a world into which no one else had entry and the language he used was a special language. Only the creatures of his imagination and the birds and animals were real to him and did not contend with him.

I grew more and more convinced that Mudiyanse was not the *pissu miniha*, the mad man, that others called him. He had more sensitivity and intelligence than many of the people I mingled with both on the housing estate as well as from the village. He was less selfish. He had no greed for the possessions of others. He had displaced no one. He himself was the one who was displaced. He had a deep knowledge of the land, of birds, animals and all living creatures. He had so much understanding of plants and their growing. If only, I thought, he had his own plot of paddy, if only he could gather his harvest, thresh it on the kamatha, if only . . . His woeful pleas always went unheeded. People had ceased to listen and had shut him out of their lives. They failed to realize that the land was in his blood. He was essentially a *goviya*, a farmer. To cultivate his fields was an affirmation of his roots, the inheritance of the land to which he belonged and to which he was so deeply attached. His need for his paddy field to till, to garner his grain, was not a desire for possession but a call of his very being. But no one understood. The obsession was graven into his mind, his brain.

Even then, I did not know how much he had suffered for his lands. His brothers had sent him away to a mental asylum when his demands had grown too insistent. This story came out one day when my daughter asked him why he had no teeth. It was the electric shocks at the asylum, he explained. 'The piece of rubber they insert when they give the shocks kept slipping out of my mouth. I felt all my teeth rattling and when I awoke, it was into a new world.'

I wondered sometimes whether it was the treatment which had caused this change. 'Why did they take you there?' I asked.

'I don't know why,' he said. 'I used to wander about in

138

the village plucking breadfruit, and here and there a coconut. The people began to say "pissu, pissu". I was not mad at all. I can't understand what happened. One day they fastened manacles on my wrists and I was taken away. While I was there, in the asylum, my whole body would tremble when I was subjected to the electric shocks treatment. My teeth chattered and shook. Some of the others never regained consciousness. Those of us who came out of it were given milk, eggs and good nourishing food.

'Even my woman was chased away from the village. She was an orphan like myself. I met her one day on the bund of the lake. I said to her, "Will you come and live with me, cook my food, wash my clothes?" "Yes," she said. "I have no home, nowhere to go. You look like a kind man, one who will care for me. Men have hurt me. We are both all alone in the world."

'She came with me to the village and we lived together. But she was an outsider, she did not belong to this village. These people were afraid of outsiders. They were afraid of what my sons would do if they were born in this village. It would mean that there would be claims to the inheritance. They would be strong enough to stake their claims . . . so they took me away. Nor did they allow her to live in peace. They drove her out of the village. When I returned she had disappeared.'

He had spent five years in the asylum. He had been taken away in chains, kept in chains. It was only when he had signed papers saying that he had no claim to his brother's fields that he had been released and allowed to come back to the village.

139

I felt an overwhelming sense of horror and pity when I heard this story. How could they? He had not hurt anyone. It was others who hurt him, sensing his vulnerability and his lack of physical strength, his inability to avert attacks on himself. He didn't have any means of protecting himself from their jibes. He was not like the people of the village. They must have found his inner strength and his power to survive unacceptable. And so now they called him a madman. One day I heard some of the village children taunting him: *kimbula*, crocodile, they called out. The animal image had its special connotations of fear and threat. They were thrusting him out of their community into the world of the predator. Often, children would throw stones at him and run away. Or they would climb his trees and steal his fruit. The elders in the community would address him in derisive tones, mocking and taunting him.

'What will happen to Mudiyanse?' I once asked Kiriamma, who would cut grass for her cattle from my garden.

'Oh, he will just die,' she said, 'and be buried under the thambili tree with his father.' It sounded callous, but seemed right in a way for Mudiyanse to go back to the earth, his obsession buried with him. Some strange plant would grow out of the loam and spread its tendrils all over.

She told me the story of the day he had gone mad. She had been a little girl then, but she remembered it vividly. He had had a bitter quarrel with his grandmother and had lost control of himself. He wandered around, searching for water to cool his anger, and finally immersed himself in the water tank. But even this was not enough, and he ran to the river

140

and dived in. He spent days in the river, feeling the currents flow over his body, until the fires that threatened to consume him were put out. It was only then that anyone had the courage to approach him, to take him away to the asylum.

In all the time that he spent with me, I had never noticed any signs of his madness as such. But there was one word which obsessed him, and gradually it begun to register upon my ear, within my consciousness, in its constant reiteration, in its obsessive re-echoing. Paminilla, paminilla.

'Mudiyanse, what is all this again about your paminilla, your petition and your ferocious threats of cutting up people?' I asked him one day.

'Don't you know what they have done again? Taken my paddy. Not given me my share of the harvest. I'll cut them all up . . . wait and see . . .'

Sometimes, listening to his importunate pleas about his paminilla, we felt we had to help him.

'Show us the deeds, Mudiyanse,' we said.

'What deeds do I need? All that land is mine. My own people have taken it all from me. Didn't my father carry me and bring me all the way to Watapuluwa and build his house here? Wasn't he buried under the thambili tree from which I still pluck the golden bunches of nuts?'

On some days, as soon as he saw any of us, Mudiyanse would go on endlessly. 'These thieves have taken my paddy again. This time, too, they have stolen what is rightfully mine. This time, I'll get a gun, a sword, and cut them up. Mahatthmaya, tomorrow I'll come early, help me to write my paminilla.'

'Yes, yes,' my husband would say to placate him.

141

'Tomorrow we will write it for you'.

But then he would forget. Sometimes his anger and determination would die even as he expressed it. Once, my brother had come to visit me. We were sitting in the veranda, talking idly and watching the dusk creep in over the trees and fields. Mudiyanse came up the road to our house at that moment, breathing fire.

'Mudiyanse,' I called out, 'what is the matter?'

'I am going to prepare the paminilla. Or I will take an axe and kill them. Mahatthmaya, will you write this petition for me? This season, too, they have taken my share of paddy. They have cheated me out of one hundred and seventy-five bushels. When I go and ask for my share, they scold me, they beat me . . .'

I introduced him to my brother. Mudiyanse promptly invited my brother to see his plot of land.

My brother was curious. 'Where does he live?' he asked.

'Behind our house, in the village. But it's difficult and dangerous at this hour. Mudiyanse, my brother is not used to that pathway. It's too steep and precipitous. You can take him to your plot of land the next time he comes, in daytime.'

'Yes, the next time I come to Kandy, I will visit you,' my brother promised. 'You should come and visit me in Mahawa.'

'Can I come to your estate, mahatthmaya? Really?'

'Yes, Mudiyanse, you will be most welcome. You can eat the fish from the wewa and the rice from my fields.'

'You are sure, mahatthmaya? I can come, can't I? It must be a good life there with your paddy fields, the coconut plantation, the mango and guava trees. But see my own plight. My own people have deprived me of my inheritance, my share of the paddy fields. I'll come and live with you on your land in Mahawa.'

But we knew he loved the village too much to ever leave it. He loved the land, though all his experiences had been bitter. His dreams were such simple ones. He wanted more than anything else to sow his own paddy and eat rice he had harvested from his own fields. He wanted to work in his own field, to drive his buffalo along the grassy paths, he wanted to sow the seed and gather the harvest, thresh the grain and carry it to the rice mill in Mawilmada. This was his all-consuming desire but we knew it would never happen. He was doomed to carry sacks of the bounty of other people's harvests but never his own.

It was only my family that listened to him. We knew what it was to be displaced. We too had had the experience of losing our land bit by bit, of always having to live in rented houses as tenants, at the mercy of landlords. But when we talked about it, people would listen and sympathize. Mudiyanse had no one but us to listen to him.

So as I listened to him, I would think of words of consolation I could never utter. Yes, Mudiyanse, I understand. It's the way of the world. None of us get our due shares of anything. Look at me . . . do I have a house or land of my own? No, I too possess nothing. Others have taken over my house and property. We are both people who have been deprived of an inheritance. We suffer for it. I cannot stay permanently in anyone's house . . . We are asked to go at the will of the landlord . . . But what can you and I do? Who will listen to us? At least you have a little patch of earth with a hut and some trees you can call your own, I have nothing . . .

One day, he was plucking fruit from our avocado tree. He knew instinctively which would be ripe. I thought I heard voices in the garden, so I went outside.

'Mudiyanse, has anyone come?' I asked.

There was no one to be seen.

'Mudiyanse, did you hear voices?' I looked up at the tree. 'Were you talking to anyone?'

'I am telephoning a friend who lives on the other side of the valley,' he said from his perch on one of the topmost branches. He continued the conversation. 'Hullo, hullo? How are you today? When are you coming to see me? I'll pluck some fresh thambili for you when you arrive. I have still to get my paddy. I am entitled to so many bushels. These people are cultivating my fields and will not give me my share.'

No, Mudiyanse was not mad at all. He never had been. Somehow when he had returned, he had learned to survive in his dwelling by the thambili tree where the guardian spirit of his father protected him. His roots were deep, deep in the ancient village among the rustling reptiles that uncoiled their length and sheltered along the roads and grassy banks, the king crows with their ruby red eyes, the wild hare and mongoose.

Almost every time that he came to our house, we would give him something to eat. By way of thanks, he would say, 'Then tomorrow I will bring you some *kurumba*, young coconuts.' His words concealed his embarrassment at taking something for which he could not repay in kind. I have eight good thambili. After all, I can give two, can't I? I don't need money for that.' Or he would bring mangoes, breadfruit or avocado pears.

'Sell these and earn some money for yourself,' we would tell him.

During the Sinhala New Year, someone gave him some newly harvested *kekulu* rice. He brought the bag to our house and sat sifting a handful of grain in his palms. 'What am I to do with this? You keep it.'

'Then we shall make kiribath and keep your share,' I said, accepting his gift. 'Don't forget to come tomorrow.'

'Yes,' he said, 'I will come early in the morning.'

We prepared the dish of milk rice, cut it into diamond shapes and kept it at the breakfast table. But Mudiyanse did not come till late that night.

'Mudiyanse,' we said, 'where were you this morning? We have kept your share of the kiribath. Sit down and eat.'

We tried to find him more work so that he could earn more. He worked hard at his jobs—cutting grass, carrying sacks of paddy for those who had their lands in the village. He would work till late in the night, compulsively, the sweat streaming down his body. He was always eager to help though sometimes he did things that were contrary to what was wanted. He had uprooted all the blue grass in my friend Bianca's garden, which she had planted with such great care.

'Mudiyanse, what have you done?' she exclaimed in horror when she returned home.

'Don't worry, I'll replant it all. It will grow again,' he said. He replanted it blade by blade, but it never took root again.

Almost every morning he would come to our garden and call out 'Mahatthmaya?' I would greet him and ask him if he wanted tea. I would pour the tea, made with fresh tea leaves, and stir in the milk and sugar. He would never drink the tea which our cook Freda made. He felt that the tea was stale, the water had not been boiled sufficiently, that she was sparing of milk and sugar. If Freda made the tea, he would take one sip and pour the cup of tea into the drain. 'Look at this man,' Freda would complain 'wasting a good cup of tea. He doesn't trust me at all.'

He was a natural gardener. He had green fingers. Whatever he planted flourished. His hands were happy when they touched the earth. 'Look,' my husband said, 'the plantain suckers he set down at that end of the garden have taken root and are going to bear good fruit.' The plantain flowers were encased in a sheath of deep people. A squirrel was sucking the honey from the florets. We shared the bunch of plantains with Mudiyanse.

I would occasionally get him to carry things from me to my father, who lived in the city, as another means of earning. After a few times, my father wrote to me, 'Don't send that man here. He worries me. When the boxes of mangoes came from the estate in Mahawa, he just carries on eating them without a pause. After the box is over, he importunes me for more. Don't send him. He keeps pestering me.'

One day my father sent some choice kitul jaggery that my aunt Elsie sent him through Mudiyanse. Some days passed. Mudiyanse did not come back. Then a postcard arrived with a terse message: 'Sir, I am sorry I couldn't come. I am very ill. I was waylaid by thieves. They beat me up and robbed me of all I possessed. All the jaggery I carried with me was stolen.'

The postcard came from Watapuluwa. He couldn't face us. Later we heard that he had sold the jaggery at half price in the village. But he couldn't live without us and gradually drifted back into our lives.

During the kerosene shortage, there were long queues. One day Mudiyanse was sent with money and two plastic gallon-containers to buy oil for us. He disappeared once more. We were desperate to cook food and finally collected sticks to make a fire in the hearth and boil rice. Eyes tearing and smarting with the smoke, we had to make do.

Rumours started circulating. Mudiyanse had been seen standing in the queue. He had been seen in the suburb of Katugastota, in Colombo Street, at the petrol station in Kandy, at an eating house, at a hotel . . .

Once more Mudiyanse drifted back. He looked around the garden as if nothing had happened. 'We'll cut the jak fruit. The fruit looks ripe . . .'

'Mudiyanse, where were you? Where's the kerosene? The plastic containers?' We were only poor teachers and money was scarce in our household. It came out after a while that he had sold the containers, and with that money and that which he had given him for the oil, he had gone to a hotel and had a hearty meal.

'Mudiyanse, why did you do this to us? The children were hungry . . .

'I was hungry.'

We had to accept his terse explanation.

Mudiyanse loved sweet things—bread and butter with sugar and jam. He didn't like *pol sambol* or hot curries. He loved fruit too. A ripe papaya vanished off the tree. The milk was still oozing out where the fruit had been snapped off from its stalk.

'Mudiyanse, where is that fruit? We were saving it for my daughter's birthday. You plucked it, didn't you?'

'Mmm, yes, I plucked it. I was hungry. It wasn't ripe enough. My tongue feels sore after eating it.'

'Mudiyanse, how can you say that? The fruits on that tree are as sweet as nectar. It must have been delicious . . .'

'Hmmn!' he murmured. 'Not sweet enough. My tongue feels grazed.'

After each such episode, he would come back and sit with a book at the table on the veranda, reading and carrying on his monologue. If you answered, he would start all over again. 'This year too I was deprived of my paddy harvest.'

A part of Mudiyanse wanted very much to be part of village life. I could sympathize with that because we too felt like outsiders. We too were seldom invited anywhere. But unlike us, Mudiyanse would go. When there was a funeral going on in a house, he would stand outside in the garden, peering through the windows. No one welcomed him inside their houses, even if he came as a mourner. Everyone would be dressed in white, sitting upright in straight-backed chairs, wearing stern expressions to show how seriously they took death. Mudiyanse would be clad in his usual sweat- and mud-stained shirt. If it was cold, he would be wearing two shirts instead of the one. He always looked like one of those old weathered scarecrows that flapped its loose sleeves in the wind, alone in the paddy field with birds screeching about its head. His sinewy legs emerged from his loose khaki shorts; he wore odd leather shoes without laces. Yet he never stayed away from a funeral. He felt it was his duty to go and pay his respects. Everyone in the housing estate knew him, and he had at one time or another worked for almost everyone here. He would come to our house and announce, 'Today there is a funeral. I must go.'

Although Mudiyanse was never invited into the houses of those people on the housing estate, it was he who cut, chopped and stacked the firewood for every festive occasion. On the day of almsgiving, *dana*, he told me he was to work all day at the house of a retired bureaucrat. That evening, he came to my house and said he was hungry.

'Mudiyanse, you cut all that firewood today and you say you are hungry. Didn't you get a share of the dana?'

He spoke hesitantly, 'There were many guests . . . the others were eating . . . It was getting late . . . they must have forgotten me . . .'

When he worked in our garden, he would never think of how many hours he had spent at his unceasing labour. We had to tell him, 'It's time now to stop. It's getting dark.' He would then put his tools away, accept his wages and set out to the township for his evening drink. If he had money, he would go out and eat, and after that come and tell us about it.

'I went to the *apana salawa* in town. I had rice and curry. It cost me twelve rupees.'

'Why so much?'

'I also ate a fried fish, a *salaya*. I had an egg too. And tea.'

On other days, he would arrive and announce, 'Today I have had no work.'

'Mudiyanse, are you hungry?

149

He would not answer. Silence meant affirmation.

'Would you like some hot tea?'

'Ah yes, tea with plenty of milk and sugar, that would be good.' He would settle down with his tea and books.

I think I felt a strong sense of similarity between our lives and his. We too were striving to survive on the little we earned, standing for long hours at bus stands, queuing to draw our small monthly wages. We were alien in a society which was close-knit and kept us at the fringe. We were never invited for the weddings or festivals on the housing estate. Festive trays of sweetmeats, covered with the ceremonial white cloth, would be borne to all the houses except ours. Very occasionally, a tray would come for us at Christmas time. The few Christian families had carols by candlelight, 'pound and pint' parties and prayer meetings, but most of the families soon emigrated to Australia or moved out of the housing estate, and these occasions came to an end too.

'How can we grumble?' my daughter would say. 'Look at Mudiyanse who somehow survives and shows no greed or desire for anyone's possessions.'

We moved from Watapuluwa to the town but Mudiyanse remained a part of our lives. He would come walking all the way from to town whenever he felt lonely or had news to give us or had need of us. Every season, he would come to pluck our fruit. Mudiyanse had always been a great climber of trees, no one was as skilled and adept at reaching the topmost branches. Even the young men of the village were not as good as he was at plucking mangoes, avocado pears, breadfruit and bunches of king coconuts from the laden trees of the housing estate. Mudiyanse himself did not want to admit that he was now too weak, too old from years of privation, for climbing trees. It was something he would never give up. Even where we were concerned, we could never accept the fact that Mudiyanse was growing old. When the *rambutans* or mangoes were ready for picking, we would say, 'When will Mudiyanse come? There's no one else who can go up those trees.' But when he climbed high on the trees, I would call out again and again. 'Mudiyanse, please, please be careful, you can eat as many mangoes as you want when you come down from the tree. Watch out, don't climb any higher, the branch may give way. Don't fall, it doesn't matter if you don't pluck any more. What we have is enough.' But there was nothing he loved more than sitting on a branch, eating the ripe fruit and throwing the skins down. He was in his element then. The tall soaring trees were always places where he could be happiest, away from the earth and stony paths which bruised his feet. Talking to the wind. Talking to himself, the person who hurt him least. From the vantage point of the treetop, the whole world lay beneath him, we were dwarfed and diminished by the stature he assumed up there, far above us, looking down on us, we who could never reach that safe eyrie, never metamorphose as he did into another shape and form.

One morning, his niece Dhammika came to tell us that Mudiyanse had died. He had fallen off a tall coconut tree, clutching onto a frond which had given way, they said. He had already plucked some of the nuts. Dhammika said that the woman for whom he had been plucking the coconuts had taken some of them into the house before all the nuts had been gathered. 'She should not have done so. It is the custom not to take the plucked nuts inside until everything has been gathered together and the person plucking them has climbed down from the tree. That's the way we do it according to tradition.'

And moreover, Dhammika said that the woman, instead of expressing regret or pity, had complained about his work. 'I told him not to climb the tree. He didn't even pluck thambili. Only kurumba, the nuts which were not yet matured.'

The last time he had visited us, sauntering into the garden as he usually did with that casual yet regal gait as if he had all the time in the world, he had husked some coconuts for me. They still lay in a corner of the veranda, a reminder of that presence which had been among us for so many years, at all times, both good and bad.

I looked once again at the coconuts husked by his hands and thought of him. Was it then his karma to die as he did? My hope was that he would be reborn again to live a life that was full of all that he had been denied—friendship, the love of kith and kin, books to read, good food to eat, shelter. Would Mudiyanse find himself in another birth, would he return to this world again? Would he go through this process of *uppajjati*, the cycles of rebirth? Who could foretell? Mudiyanse had harmed no one. Rather, it was he had been harmed, his birthright and property taken away by greed, duplicity and stealth.

If he were reborn, it would be, I felt convinced, to a better life. Mudiyanse never destroyed living things. He was never covetous or cruel. People had always taken what little had belonged to him, mocking and taunting him all the while. For Mudiyanse, there would never be either the torments of hell or birth among the creeping animals. His deeds would be his reward and according to the five Gatis, he would be born into the realm of mankind where other privileged people would meet him and learn from him. Such would be the continuity of his life until that final flame of being was extinguished.

He had forced upon us a recognition of himself, he compelled us to recognize his existence. When he told me the stories of his life, the past began to unravel itself, like a Jataka tale. It dawned upon my consciousness that this was a man who was travelling in the ocean of samsara. This was a brief sojourn, on this earth, through this passage with all its travails, all its trials and tribulations. He was truly one of nature's last innocents.

READ MORE IN PENGUIN

In every corner of the world, on every subject under the sun, Penguin represents quality and variety—the very best in publishing today.

For complete information about books available from Penguin—including Puffins, Penguin Classics and Arkana—and how to order them, write to us at the appropriate address below. Please note that for copyright reasons the selection of books varies from country to country.

In India: Please write to *Penguin Books India Pvt. Ltd. 11 Community Centre, Panchsheel Park, New Delhi 110017*

In the United Kingdom: Please write to *Dept JC, Penguin Books Ltd. Bath Road, Harmondsworth, West Drayton, Middlesex, UB7 ODA. UK*

In the United States: Please write to *Penguin Putnam Inc., 375 Hudson Street, New York, NY 10014*

In Canada: Please write to *Penguin Books Canada Ltd. 10 Alcorn Avenue, Suite 300, Toronto, Ontario M4V 3B2*

In Australia: Please write to *Penguin Books Australia Ltd. 487, Maroondah Highway, Ring Wood, Victoria 3134*

In New Zealand: Please write to *Penguin Books (NZ) Ltd. Private Bag, Takapuna, Auckland 9*

In the Netherlands: Please write to *Penguin Books Netherlands B.V., Keizersgracht 231 NL-1016 DV Amsterdom*

In Germany : Please write to *Penguin Books Deutschland GmbH, Metzlerstrasse 26, 60595 Frankfurt am Main, Germany*

In Spain: Please write to *Penguin Books S.A., Bravo Murillo, 19-1'B, E-28015 Madrid, Spain*

In Italy: Please write to *Penguin Italia s.r.l., Via Felice Casati 20, I-20104 Milano*

In France: Please write to *Penguin France S.A., 17 rue Lejeune, F-31000 Toulouse*

In Japan: Please write to *Penguin Books Japan. Ishikiribashi Building, 2-5-4, Suido, Tokyo 112*

In Greece: Please write to *Penguin Hellas Ltd, dimocritou 3, GR-106 71 Athens*

In South Africa: Please write to *Longman Penguin Books Southern Africa (Pty) Ltd, Private Bag X08, Bertsham 2013*

THE SANDGLASS

Romesh Gunesekera

From the author of *Reef*, shortlisted for the Booker Prize in 1994, comes a stunning new novel and a masterpiece of storytelling.

When Prins Ducal arrives in London for his mother Pearl's funeral, he is full not only of grief but of unanswered questions about the past. Among the secrets that his mother has taken with her to the grave is the mystery of his father's publicized 'accidental death' nearly forty years earlier. Memories bubble slowly to the surface as he tries to uncover the truth with his friend Chip who, as Pearl's ex-lodger and confidant, has assumed the role of keeper of the Ducals' secrets.

Profoundly moving and often sharply funny, *The Sandglass* unravels the many stories of transformation, disappearance and loss that haunt the Ducal family from the moment Pearl's husband purchases his dream-house—Arcadia—which lies at the centre of both the Vatunas estate and a bitter feud. It follows Pearl's courageous flight from her homeland and traces the consequences of her children's efforts to find their own dreamlands in England, America and modern-day Sri Lanka.

The Sandglass is an intricate novel of love and longing that transforms the world we know into one we wish to know more about; a world in which hope has to survive the darkest truths.

THE JAM FRUIT TREE
Carl Muller

Hilarious, affectionate, candid and moving, this is the story of the Burghers of Sri Lanka . . .

Who are the Burghers? Descended from the Dutch, the Portuguese, the British and other foreigners who arrived in the island-nation of Sri Lanka (and 'mingled' with the local inhabitants), the Burghers often stand out because of their curiously mixed features—grey eyes in an otherwise Dravid face, for instance . . . A handsome and guileless people, the Burghers have always lived it up, forever willing to 'put a party'.

Carl Muller, a Burgher himself, writes in this quasi-fictional, engaging biography of the lives of his people; they emerge, at the end of his story, as a race of fun-loving, hardy people, much like the jam fruit tree which simply refuses to be contained or destroyed.

YAKADA YAKĀ

Carl Muller

Yakada Yakā is the second part of the Burgher trilogy that began with *The Jam Fruit Tree* . . .

When the conquering British roll out the first railway steam-driver locomotive in Sri Lanka, it causes quite a stir. The smoke-spewing, banshee-wailing, fearsome black thing hisses like a thousand cobras . . . and the villagers declare that this Thing is an Iron Demon—a *yakada yakā*.

The Burghers who drive these Iron Demons have a penchant for challenging authority and courting trouble, sometimes just to liven things up in the railway outposts . . . and so it is that Sonnaboy and Meerwald chase a large group of villagers all across Anuradhapura, mother-naked but not much bothered by it, Ben Godlieb conjures up a corpse in his cowcatcher, Dickie Byrd single-handedly demolishes a Pentecostal Mission and is hailed as the messiah of the Railway fraternity, and Basil Van der Smaght filches a human heart and feeds it to the Nawalapitiya railway staff . . . and to cap it all, Sonnaboy takes French leave to act in *The Bridge on the River Kwai*!

'(Muller) tells his tale with a gentle humour often bordering on tenderness, but couched in the vigorous rugged localese. Almost immediately we find ourselves empathising with Muller's roistering band that sins and prays with equal zest.'

—*Business Standard*

'. . . The Burghers . . . believed in living life to the hilt. Every situation occasioned wild revels, and there was nothing that could not be solved through a brawl.'

—*India Today*

ONCE UPON A TENDER TIME

Carl Muller

***Once Upon a Tender Time**,* **a poignant tale of childhood, is the concluding part of Carl Muller's Burgher trilogy.**

The Burghers of Sri Lanka, hardy and fun-loving, produce children by the dozen—but often forget them. Carloboy Prins von Bloss and his companions are usually considered a pain in the neck by the adults they encounter as they go about the serious business of discovering the world and, primarily, the facts of life. Romps in the backyard, trysts in deserted houses and long bicycle rides to discover true love are commonplace. Also frequent are thrashings and canings as adults try to discipline these 'devils'. But there are happier moments too—vacations spent roaming and hunting in the beautiful Sri Lankan jungles; trips to the favourite bookshop to browse and perhaps buy the latest Captain Marvel comic; and the signal honour of riding on the engine because dad is the engine driver . . .

Unusual, enchanting and unforgettable, this memoir of a singular childhood should further enhance the award-winning author's already considerable reputation.

SPIT AND POLISH

Carl Muller

'See here, first take a little polish on the finger and rub into the
leather. Then spit . . . and rub . . .'—boasts one recruit of his
boot polishing skills . . . sadly, the only reward this gets him is
thirty pairs of shoes to shine . . .

This is only one of the hilarious episodes in Carl Muller's continuation
of the von Bloss family saga. Carloboy von Bloss is back, now a
robust young man of eighteen, spending four eventful years in the
one-ship Royal Ceylon Navy. Carloboy and his fellow recruits get
up to the weirdest capers: painting their boots black; posing as
Italian ghosts; planning to wink at Queen Elizabeth II who is to take
the salute at the Royal Parade at Colombo; going on surreptitious
trysts with the police inspector's neice . . . of course with plenty
of beer to keep them company.

Interspersed with these comic episodes are chapters which retell the
forgotten events of World War II—the Pacific manoeuvres which at
times seemed godsent, and Japan's humiliating defeat at the hands
of the Allied powers.

Spit and Polish is a fascinating and light-hearted account of Burgher
life in Sri Lanka, poignantly written by an acclaimed author who is
a Burgher himself. Sparkling with wit and written with an unerring
sense of drama, this book is a veritable treat for Carl Muller fans
as well as for those reading him for the first time.

COLOMBO: A NOVEL

Carl Muller

'Colombo is in the throes of an explosion. Its face changes continuously, its vices are legion, its future as yet obscure and its paths speak of sunlight as well as of shadow . . .'

Carl Muller begins his quasi-fictional portrait of this beautiful, war-torn city by describing the great battles fought over it by European colonizers . . . In AD 1505, a Portuguese fleet blown off course took shelter in Galle, overthrew the local kings, fortified Colombo and decided to stay. The Dutch came along, ousted the Portuguese, made Colombo their capital and ruled till the British arrived and sent them packing. Muller intersperses the tales of the past into descriptions of the battles that are being fought in Colombo today— political battles in which vested interests play a major role as well as battles fought on the individual level in the struggle to survive: young women and children turning to prostitution to earn an extra buck, people begging in the streets to make ends meet, unemployed young men turning to crime in frustration, students demonstrating against atrocities, lovers pining for nightfall in order to push away loneliness if only for a few moments . . . Written in Muller's lucid style, *Colombo: A Novel* is a chronicle of a city's trials and triumphs.

FUNNY BOY

Shyam Selvadurai

In the world of his large family, affluent Tamils living in Colombo, Arjie is an oddity . . .

Arjie is a 'funny boy' who prefers dressing as a girl to playing cricket with his older brother. In *Funny Boy* we follow the life of the family through Arjie's eyes as he struggles to come to terms both with his own homosexuality and with the racism of the society in which he lives. In the north of Sri Lanka there's a war going on between the army and the Tamil Tigers, and gradually it begins to encroach on the family's comfortable life. Sporadic acts of violence flare into full-scale riots and lead ultimately to tragedy.

Written in clear, simple prose, and masterly in its mingling of the personal and the political, *Funny Boy*, marks the arrival of an exceptional new novelist, a writer with a profound understanding of the human heart.

IF THE MOON SMILED

Chandani Lokugé

I go down to the river, unheeding my mother's disapproval. I dip into the lazily flowing water. Here, at least, nothing has changed. The bath-cloth ballons around my body and I press it down. I loosen my hair and let it spread where it will. I open my hands upwards on the water's surface, languidly remembering. All, all that is familiar. The promise. The promise of life.

As a young woman in Sri Lanka, Manthri marvels at the promise of life and yearns for a future of fulfilled dreams. Years on, she finds herself in a loveless marriage, in a foreign land, and estranged from her two Australian children. Torn between an idyllic past to which she cannot return and a present that breaks her heart, she never loses touch with those dreams, nor abandons her passionate enchantment with life.

If the Moon Smiled is a stirring and lyrical novel, a poignant tale about the powerful bonds that shape a woman's life.